Non-Football Supporters' Guide & Yearbook 2017

EDITOR
John Robinson

Twenty-fifth Edition

For details of our range of 2,200 books and over 300 DVDs, visit our web site or contact us using the information shown below.

British Library Cataloguing in Publication Data
A catalogue record for this book is available from the British Library

ISBN: 978-1-86223-336-2

The Publishers, and the Football Clubs itemised are unable to accept liability for any loss, damage or injury caused by error or inaccuracy in the information published in this guide.

Manufactured in the UK by Ashford Colour Press Ltd.

FOREWORD

Our thanks go to the numerous club officials who have aided us in the compilation of information contained in this guide as well as John Mills (for photographs of the AFC Fylde and FC United of Manchester grounds), Michael Robinson (page layouts), Bob Budd (cover artwork) and Tony Brown (Cup Statistics – www.soccerdata.com).

Any readers who have up-to-date ground photographs which they would like us to consider for use in a future edition of this guide are requested to contact us at our address which is shown on the facing page.

The fixtures listed later in this book were released just a short time before we went to print and, as such, some of the dates shown may be subject to change. We therefore suggest that readers treat these fixtures as a rough guide and check dates carefully before attending matches.

We would like to wish our readers a safe and happy spectating season.

John Robinson
EDITOR

CONTENTS

The Vanarama National League Clubs & Information 5-29

The Vanarama National League North Clubs & Information 30-52

The Vanarama National League South Clubs & Information 53-75

2015/2016 Statistics for the National League 76

2015/2016 Statistics for the National League North 77

2015/2016 Statistics for the National League South 78

2015/2016 Statistics for the Evo-Stik Northern League Premier Division 79

2015/2016 Statistics for the Evo-Stik Southern League – Premier Division .. 80

2015/2016 Statistics for the Ryman Football League Premier Division 81

2015/2016 F.A. Trophy Results 82-86

2015/2016 F.A. Vase Results 87-91

2016/2017 Season Fixtures for the Vanarama National League 92-94

Advertisement: The Non-League Club Directory 2017 95

Advertisement: The Supporters' Guide Series 96

THE VANARAMA NATIONAL LEAGUE

Address   4th Floor, 20 Waterloo Street, Birmingham   B2 5TB

Phone (0121) 643-3143

Web site   www.footballconference.co.uk

Clubs for the 2016/2017 Season

Aldershot Town FC .... Page 6
Barrow FC .... Page 7
Boreham Wood FC .... Page 8
Braintree Town FC .... Page 9
Bromley FC .... Page 10
Chester FC .... Page 11
Dagenham & Redbridge FC .... Page 12
Dover Athletic FC .... Page 13
Eastleigh FC .... Page 14
Forest Green Rovers FC .... Page 15
Gateshead FC .... Page 16
Guiseley FC .... Page 17
Lincoln City FC .... Page 18
Macclesfield Town .... Page 19
Maidstone United FC .... Page 20
North Ferriby United FC .... Page 21
Solihull Moors FC .... Page 22
Southport FC .... Page 23
Sutton United FC .... Page 24
Torquay United FC .... Page 25
Tranmere Rovers FC .... Page 26
Woking FC .... Page 27
Wrexham AFC .... Page 28
York City FC .... Page 29

ALDERSHOT TOWN FC

Founded: 2013 (as a new company)
Former Names: Aldershot Town FC
Nickname: 'Shots'
Ground: Ebb Stadium, High Street, Aldershot, GU11 1TW
Record Attendance: 7,500 (18th November 2000)
Pitch Size: 117 × 76 yards

Colours: Red shirts with Blue shorts
Telephone Nº: (01252) 320211
Fax Number: (01252) 339389
Club Secretary: (01252) 320211– Bob Green
Ground Capacity: 6,500
Seating Capacity: 2,042
Web site: www.theshots.co.uk
E-mail: admin@theshots.co.uk

GENERAL INFORMATION

Supporters Club: c/o Club
Telephone Nº: (01252) 320211
Car Parking: Parsons Barracks Car Park is adjacent
Coach Parking: Contact the club for information
Nearest Railway Station: Aldershot (5 mins. walk)
Nearest Bus Station: Aldershot (5 minutes walk)
Club Shop: At the ground
Opening Times: Saturday matchdays 10.00am to 2.45pm and 9.30am to 7.30pm on Tuesday matchdays.
Telephone Nº: (01252) 320211

GROUND INFORMATION

Away Supporters' Entrances & Sections:
Accommodation in the East Bank Terrace, Bill Warren section (South Stand) – Redan Hill Turnstiles Nº 11 and 12.

ADMISSION INFO (2016/2017 PRICES)

Adult Standing: £17.00   **Adult Seating**: £19.00
Ages 11 to 16 Standing: £5.00
Ages 11 to 16 Seating: £7.00
Note: Under-11s are admitted free with paying adults – a maximum of 2 children per adult.
Concessionary Standing: £13.00
Concessionary Seating: £15.00
Note: Military personnel are charged Concessionary prices
Programme Price: £3.00

DISABLED INFORMATION

Wheelchairs: Accommodated in both the North Stand and the away section
Helpers: Admitted
Prices: £13.00 for the disabled, free of charge for helpers
Disabled Toilets: Available
Contact: (01252) 320211 (Bookings are required)

Travelling Supporters' Information:
Routes: From the M3: Exit at Junction 4 and follow signs for Aldershot (A331). Leave the A331 at the A323 exit (Ash Road) and continue along into the High Street. The ground is just past the Railway Bridge on the right; From the A31: Continue along the A31 to the junction with the A331, then as above; From the A325 (Farnborough Road): Follow signs to the A323 then turn left into Wellington Avenue. The ground is just off the 2nd roundabout on the left – the floodlights are clearly visible.

BARROW FC

Founded: 1901
Former Names: None
Nickname: 'Bluebirds'
Ground: Furness Building Society Stadium, Barrow-in-Furness, Cumbria LA14 5UW
Record Attendance: 16,874 (1954)
Pitch Size: 110 × 75 yards

Colours: White shirts with Blue shorts
Telephone N°: (01229) 666061
Ground Capacity: 4,057
Seating Capacity: 928
Web site: www.barrowafc.com
E-mail: office@barrowafc.com

GENERAL INFORMATION

Car Parking: Street Parking, Popular Side Car Park and Soccer Bar Car Park
Coach Parking: Adjacent to the ground
Nearest Railway Station: Barrow Central (½ mile)
Nearest Bus Station: ½ mile
Club Shop: At the ground
Opening Times: Monday to Friday 9.00am – 3.30pm and Saturdays 10.00am – 2.00pm
Telephone N°: (01229) 666061

GROUND INFORMATION

Away Supporters' Entrances & Sections:
West Terrace (not covered)

ADMISSION INFO (2016/2017 PRICES)

Adult Standing: £14.00
Adult Seating: £17.00
Concessionary Standing: £12.00
Concessionary Seating: £11.00
Ages 11 to 17 Standing/Seating: £5.00
Under-11s Standing/Seating: £1.00

DISABLED INFORMATION

Wheelchairs: 6 spaces available in the Disabled Area
Helpers: Admitted
Prices: Normal prices apply
Disabled Toilets: Available
Contact: (01229) 666061   (Bookings are not necessary)

Travelling Supporters' Information:
Routes: Exit the M6 at Junction 36 and take the A590 through Ulverston. Using the bypass, follow signs for Barrow. After approximately 5 miles, turn left into Wilkie Road and the ground is on the right.

BOREHAM WOOD FC

Founded: 1948
Former Names: Boreham Rovers FC and Royal Retournez FC
Nickname: 'The Wood'
Ground: Meadow Park, Broughinge Road, Borehamwood, Hertfordshire   WD6 5AL
Record Attendance: 4,030 (2002)
Pitch Size: 112 × 72 yards

Colours: White shirts with Black shorts
Telephone N°: (0208) 953-5097
Fax Number: (0208) 207-7982
Ground Capacity: 3,960
Seating Capacity: 1,401
Web site: www.borehamwoodfootballclub.co.uk

GENERAL INFORMATION

Car Parking: At the ground or in Brook Road car park
Coach Parking: At the ground
Nearest Railway Station: Elstree & Borehamwood (1 mile)
Nearest Bus Station: Barnet
Club Shop: At the ground
Opening Times: 11.00am to 10.00pm Monday to Thursday; 11.00am to 6.00pm at weekends
Telephone N°: (0208) 953-5097

GROUND INFORMATION

Away Supporters' Entrances & Sections:
No usual segregation

ADMISSION INFO (2016/2017 PRICES)

Adult Standing: £18.00
Adult Seating: £18.00
Under-16s Standing/Seating: £8.50
Under-12s Standing/Seating: £4.00
Senior Citizen Standing/Seating: £13.00

DISABLED INFORMATION

Wheelchairs: Accommodated
Helpers: Admitted
Prices: Concessionary prices are charged for the disabled. Helpers are admitted free of charge.
Disabled Toilets: Available
Contact: (0208) 953-5097   (Bookings are necessary)

Travelling Supporters' Information:
Routes: Exit the M25 at Junction 23 and take the A1 South. After 2 miles, take the Borehamwood exit onto the dual carriageway and go over the flyover following signs for Borehamwood for 1 mile. Turn right at the Studio roundabout into Brook Road, then next right into Broughinge Road for the ground.

BRAINTREE TOWN FC

Founded: 1898
Former Names: Manor Works FC, Crittall Athletic FC, Braintree & Crittall Athletic FC and Braintree FC
Nickname: 'The Iron'
Ground: Amlin Stadium, Clockhouse Way, Braintree, Essex CM7 3RD
Record Attendance: 4,000 (May 1952)
Pitch Size: 111 × 78 yards
Ground Capacity: 4,222
Seating Capacity: 553

Colours: Orange shirts and socks with Blue shorts
Telephone Nº: (01376) 345617
Fax Number: (01376) 330976
Correspondence Address: Tom Woodley, 19A Bailey Bridge Road, Braintree CM7 5TT
Contact Telephone Nº: (01376) 326234
Web site: www.braintreetownfc.org.uk
E-mail: braintreetfc@aol.com

GENERAL INFORMATION

Car Parking: At the ground
Coach Parking: At the ground
Nearest Railway Station: Braintree (1 mile)
Nearest Bus Station: Braintree
Club Shop: At the ground
Opening Times: Matchdays only
Telephone Nº: (01376) 345617

GROUND INFORMATION

Away Supporters' Entrances & Sections:
Gates 7-8

ADMISSION INFO (2016/2017 PRICES)

Adult Standing: £15.00 – £17.00
Adult Seating: £16.00 – £18.00
Concessionary Standing: £11.00
Concessionary Seating: £12.00
Under-16s Standing: £6.00
Under-11s Standing: £4.00
Note: Prices vary depending on the category of the game

DISABLED INFORMATION

Wheelchairs: Accommodated – 6 spaces available in the Main Stand
Helpers: Admitted
Prices: Normal prices apply
Disabled Toilets: Available
Contact: (01376) 345617

Travelling Supporters' Information:
Routes: Exit the A120 Braintree Bypass at the McDonald's roundabout and follow Cressing Road northwards. The floodlights at the ground are visible on the left ½ mile into town. Turn left into Clockhouse Way then left again for the ground.

BROMLEY FC

Founded: 1892
Former Names: None
Nickname: 'Lillywhites'
Ground: The Stadium, Hayes Lane, Bromley, Kent, BR2 9EF
Record Attendance: 12,000 (24th September 1949)
Pitch Size: 112 × 72 yards

Colours: White shirts with Black shorts
Telephone Nº: (020) 8460-5291
Fax Number: (020) 8313-3992
Ground Capacity: 3,300
Seating Capacity: 1,300
Web site: www.bromleyfc.net
E-mail: info@bromleyfc.net

GENERAL INFORMATION

Car Parking: 300 spaces available at the ground
Coach Parking: At the ground
Nearest Railway Station: Bromley South (1 mile)
Nearest Bus Station: High Street, Bromley
Club Shop: At the ground
Opening Times: Matchdays only
Telephone Nº: (020) 8460-5291

GROUND INFORMATION

Away Supporters' Entrances & Sections:
No usual segregation

ADMISSION INFO (2016/2017 PRICES)

Adult Standing/Seating: £15.00
Concessionary Standing/Seating: £10.00
Under-16s/Student Standing/Seating: £5.00
Note: Under-16s are admitted free of charge with a paying adult for advance purchases up to 1 hour before kick-off.
A special £10.00 discounted price is available for Season Ticket holders of Premiership and Football League clubs.

DISABLED INFORMATION

Wheelchairs: Accommodated
Helpers: Admitted
Prices: Please phone the club for information
Disabled Toilets: Yes
Contact: (0181) 460-5291 (Bookings are necessary)

Travelling Supporters' Information:
Routes: Exit the M25 at Junction 4 and follow the A21 for Bromley and London for approximately 4 miles before forking left onto the A232 signposted for Croydon/Sutton. At the second set of traffic lights turn right into Baston Road (B265) and follow for approximately 2 miles as it becomes Hayes Street and then Hayes Lane. The ground is on the right just after a mini-roundabout.

CHESTER FC

Founded: 1885
Former Names: Chester FC and Chester City FC
Nickname: 'Blues'
Ground: Lookers Vauxhall Stadium, Bumpers Lane, Chester CH1 4LT
Pitch Size: 116 × 75 yards
Record Attendance: 5,987 (17th April 2004)

Colours: Blue and White striped shirts, Black shorts
Ground Telephone Nº: (01244) 371376
Ticket Office: (01244) 371376
Fax Number: (01244) 390265
Ground Capacity: 5,400
Seating Capacity: 4,170
Web site: www.chesterfc.com
E-mail: info@chesterfc.com

GENERAL INFORMATION

Car Parking: Ample spaces available at the ground
Coach Parking: Available at the ground
Nearest Railway Station: Chester (2 miles)
Nearest Bus Station: Chester (1½ miles)
Club Shop: At the ground
Opening Times: Weekdays & matchdays 10.00am–4.00pm
Telephone Nº: (01244) 371376

GROUND INFORMATION

Away Supporters' Entrances & Sections:
South Stand for covered seating and also part of the West Stand

ADMISSION INFO (2016/2017 PRICES)

Adult Standing: £15.00   **Adult Seating**: £18.00
Senior Citizen Standing: £10.00
Senior Citizen Seating: £12.00
Under-21s Seating/Standing: £10.00
Ages 16 and 17 Seating/Standing: £5.00
Under-16s Seating/Standing: £3.00   (Under-5s free)

DISABLED INFORMATION

Wheelchairs: 32 spaces for wheelchairs (with 40 helpers) in the West Stand and East Stand
Helpers: One helper admitted per disabled person
Prices: Normal prices for the disabled. Free for helpers
Disabled Toilets: Available in West and East Stands
Contact: (01244) 371376   (Bookings are necessary)

Travelling Supporters' Information:
Routes: From the North: Take the M56, A41 or A56 into the Town Centre and then follow Queensferry (A548) signs into Sealand Road. Turn left at the traffic lights by 'Tesco' into Bumpers Lane – the ground is ½ mile at the end of the road; From the East: Take the A54 or A51 into the Town Centre (then as North); From the South: Take the A41 or A483 into Town Centre (then as North); From the West: Take the A55, A494 or A548 and follow Queensferry signs towards Birkenhead (A494) and after 1¼ miles bear left onto the A548 (then as North); From the M6/M56 (Avoiding Town Centre): Take the M56 to Junction 16 (signposted Queensferry), turn left at the roundabout onto A5117, signposted Wales. At the next roundabout turn left onto the A5480 (signposted Chester) and after approximately 3 miles take the 3rd exit from the roundabout (signposted Sealand Road Industrial Parks). Go straight across 2 sets of traffic lights into Bumpers Lane. The ground is ½ mile on the right.

DAGENHAM & REDBRIDGE FC

Founded: 1992
Former Names: Formed by the merger of
Dagenham FC and Redbridge Forest FC
Nickname: 'The Daggers'
Ground: Chigwell Construction Stadium,
Victoria Road, Dagenham RM10 7XL
Record Attendance: 7,100 (1967)
Pitch Size: 110 × 70 yards

Colours: Red and Blue striped shirts with Blue shorts
Telephone Nº: (020) 8592-1549
Office Phone Nº: (020) 8592-7194
Secretary's Phone Nº: (020) 8592-1549
Fax Number: (020) 8593-7227
Ground Capacity: 6,078 **Seating Capacity**: 2,233
Web site: www.daggers.co.uk
E-mail: info@daggers.co.uk

GENERAL INFORMATION

Car Parking: Street parking only
Coach Parking: Street parking only
Nearest Railway Station: Dagenham East (5 mins. walk)
Nearest Bus Station: Romford
Club Shop: At the ground
Opening Times: Monday & Tuesday 12.00pm – 4.00pm;
Thursday 12.00pm – 8.00pm; Friday 12.00pm – 6.00pm;
Saturday matchdays 1.00pm – 3.00pm.
Closed on Wednesdays, Sundays and non-match Saturdays
Telephone Nº: (020) 8592-7194

GROUND INFORMATION

Away Supporters' Entrances & Sections:
Pondfield Road entrances for Pondfield Road End

ADMISSION INFO (2016/2017 PRICES)

Adult Standing: £18.00
Adult Seating: £18.00 – £21.00
Concessionary Standing: £13.00
Concessionary Seating: £13.00 – £15.00
Under-16s Standing: £10.00 (Under-10s free of charge)
Under-16s Seating: £8.00 in Family Stand
Under-10s Seating: £2.00 in Family Stand
Note: Discounts are available for tickets bought before the day
of the game and also for home fans in the Family Area

DISABLED INFORMATION

Wheelchairs: Accommodated in front of the new Stand
and the Barking College Stand
Helpers: Admitted
Prices: £12.00 for the disabled. Free of charge for Helpers
Disabled Toilets: Available at the East and West ends of the
ground and also in the Clubhouse
Contact: (020) 8592-7194 (Bookings are necessary)

Travelling Supporters' Information:
Routes: From the North & West: Take the M11 to its end and join the A406 South. At the large roundabout take the slip road
on the left signposted A13 to Dagenham. As you approach Dagenham, stay in the left lane and follow signs for A1306 signposted
Dagenham East. Turn left onto the A1112 at the 5th set of traffic lights by the McDonalds. Proceed along Ballards Road to The
Bull roundabout and bear left. Victoria Road is 450 yards on the left after passing Dagenham East tube station; From the South
& East: Follow signs for the A13 to Dagenham. Take the next slip road off signposted Elm Park & Dagenham East then turn right
at the roundabout. Go straight on at the next roundabout and turn left onto A1306. After ½ mile you will see a McDonalds on
the right. Get into the right hand filter lane and turn right onto A1112. Then as from the North & West.   **SatNav**: RM10 7XL

DOVER ATHLETIC FC

Founded: 1983
Former Names: None
Nickname: 'The Whites'
Ground: Crabble Athletic Ground, Lewisham Road, River, Dover CT17 0JB
Record Attendance: 4,186 (2002)
Pitch Size: 111 × 73 yards

Colours: White shirts with Black shorts
Telephone Nº: (01304) 822373
Fax Number: (01304) 821383
Ground Capacity: 6,500
Seating Capacity: 1,000
Web site: www.doverathletic.com
E-mail: enquiries@doverathletic.com

GENERAL INFORMATION

Car Parking: Street parking
Coach Parking: Street parking
Nearest Railway Station: Kearsney (1 mile)
Nearest Bus Station: Pencester Road, Dover (1½ miles)
Club Shop: At the ground
Opening Times: Saturdays 9.00am to 12.00pm
Telephone Nº: (01304) 822373

GROUND INFORMATION

Away Supporters' Entrances & Sections:
Segregation only used when required

ADMISSION INFO (2016/2017 PRICES)

Adult Standing: £15.00
Adult Seating: £16.50
Senior Citizen Standing: £12.00
Senior Citizen Seating: £14.00
Under-18s Standing: £6.00
Under-18s Seating: £7.50
Under-11s Standing/Seating: Free of charge

DISABLED INFORMATION

Wheelchairs: Approximately 20 spaces are available in front of the Family Stand
Helpers: Please phone the club for information
Prices: Please phone the club for information
Disabled Toilets: None
Contact: – (Bookings are not necessary)

Travelling Supporters' Information:
Routes: Take the A2 to the Whitfield roundabout and take the 4th exit. Travel down the hill to the mini-roundabout then turn left and follow the road for 1 mile to the traffic lights on the hill. Turn sharp right and pass under the railway bridge – the ground is on the left after 300 yards.

EASTLEIGH FC

Founded: 1946
Former Names: Swaythling Athletic FC and Swaythling FC
Nickname: 'The Spitfires'
Ground: The Silverlake Stadium, Stoneham Lane, Eastleigh   SO50 9HT
Record Attendance: 3,104 (2006)
Pitch Size: 112 × 74 yards

Colours: Blue shirts with White shorts
Telephone Nº: (023) 8061-3361
Fax Number: (023) 8061-2379
Ground Capacity: 6,000
Seating Capacity: 2,812 (by October 2014)
Web site: www.eastleighfc.com
e-mail: admin@eastleighfc.com

GENERAL INFORMATION
Car Parking: Spaces for 450 cars available (hard standing)
Coach Parking: At the ground
Nearest Railway Station: Southampton Parkway (¾ mile)
Nearest Bus Station: Eastleigh (2 miles)
Club Shop: At the ground
Opening Times: Matchdays and during functions only

GROUND INFORMATION
Away Supporters' Entrances & Sections:
Segregation in force for some games only. Please contact the club for further details

ADMISSION INFO (2016/2017 PRICES)
Adult Standing: £15.00
Adult Seating: £18.00
Concessionary Standing: £10.00
Concessionary Seating: £12.00
Under-16s Standing/Seating: £4.00 or £7.50
Under-7s Seating: £3.00
Note: Discounted prices are available for advance purchases

DISABLED INFORMATION
Wheelchairs: Accommodated
Helpers: Admitted
Prices: Concessionary prices apply
Disabled Toilets: Available
Contact: (023) 8061-3361   (Bookings are not necessary)

Travelling Supporters' Information:
Routes: Exit the M27 at Junction 5 (signposted for Southampton Airport) and take the A335 (Stoneham Way) towards Southampton. After ½ mile, turn right at the traffic lights into Bassett Green Road. Turn right at the next set of traffic lights into Stoneham Lane and the ground is on the right after ¾ mile.

FOREST GREEN ROVERS FC

Founded: 1889
Former Names: Stroud FC
Nickname: 'The Green Devils'
Ground: The New Lawn, Another Way,
Forest Green, Nailsworth, Gloucestershire, GL6 0FG
Record Attendance: 4,836 (3rd January 2009)
Pitch Size: 110 × 70 yards

Colours: Black and White striped shirts, Black shorts
Telephone Nº: (01453) 834860
Fax Number: (01453) 835291
Ground Capacity: 5,025
Seating Capacity: 1,881
Web site: www.forestgreenroversfc.com
E-mail: reception@forestgreenroversfc.com

GENERAL INFORMATION

Car Parking: At the ground
Coach Parking: At the ground
Nearest Railway Station: Stroud (4 miles)
Nearest Bus Station: Nailsworth
Club Shop: At the ground
Opening Times: Monday to Friday 9.00am to 3.00pm
Telephone Nº: (01453) 834860

GROUND INFORMATION

Away Supporters' Entrances & Sections:
EESI Stand

ADMISSION INFO (2016/2017 PRICES)

Adult Standing: £16.00   **Adult Seating**: £18.00–£20.00
Senior Citizen Standing: £12.00
Senior Citizen Seating: £14.00 – £16.00
Under-11s Standing/Seating: Free of charge
Young Adult Standing: £7.50
Young Adult Seating: £9.50 – £11.50
Note: Discounted prices are available for advance purchases

DISABLED INFORMATION

Wheelchairs: Accommodated in the Main Stand
Helpers: Admitted
Prices: Normal prices for the disabled. Free for helpers
Disabled Toilets: Yes
Contact: (01453) 834860   (Enquiries necessary at least 72 hours in advance)

Travelling Supporters' Information:
Routes: The ground is located 4 miles south of Stroud on the A46 to Bath. Upon entering Nailsworth, turn into Spring Hill at the mini-roundabout and the ground is approximately ½ mile up the hill on the left.

GATESHEAD FC

Founded: 1930   (Reformed in 1977)
Former Names: Gateshead United FC
Nickname: 'Tynesiders'
Ground: International Stadium, Neilson Road, Gateshead   NE10 0EF
Record Attendance: 11,750 (1995)
Pitch Size: 110 × 70 yards

Colours: White shirts with Black shorts
Telephone Nº: (0191) 478-3883
Fax Number: (0191) 440-0404
Ground Capacity: 11,750
Seating Capacity: 11,750
Web site: www.gateshead-fc.com
E-mail: info@gateshead-fc.com

GENERAL INFORMATION

Car Parking: At the stadium
Coach Parking: At the stadium
Nearest Railway Station: Gateshead Stadium Metro (½ mile); Newcastle (British Rail) 1½ miles
Nearest Bus Station: Heworth Interchange (½ mile)
Club Shop: At the stadium
Opening Times: Matchdays only
Telephone Nº: (0191) 478-3883

GROUND INFORMATION

Away Supporters' Entrances & Sections:
Tyne & Wear County Stand North End or the East Stand

ADMISSION INFO (2016/2017 PRICES)

Adult Seating: £15.00
Senior Citizen/Concessionary Seating: £10.00
Under-16s Seating: £3.00
Under-18s/Student Seating: £8.00
Note: Tickets are cheaper when purchased in advance.

DISABLED INFORMATION

Wheelchairs: 5 spaces available each for home and away fans by the trackside – Level access with automatic doors
Helpers: Admitted
Prices: Normal prices for the disabled. Helpers are admitted free of charge.
Disabled Toilets: Available in the Reception Area and on the 1st floor concourse – accessible by lift.
Contact: (0191) 478-3883   (Bookings are necessary)

Travelling Supporters' Information:
Routes: From the South: Take the A1(M) to Washington Services and fork right onto the A194(M) signposted Tyne Tunnel. At the next roundabout, turn left onto the A184 signposted for Gateshead. The Stadium is on the right after 3 miles.

GUISELEY AFC

Founded: 1909
Former Names: None
Nickname: 'The Lions'
Ground: Nethermoor Park, Otley Road, Guiseley, Leeds LS20 8BT
Record Attendance: 2,486 (1989/90)
Pitch Size: 110 × 69 yards

Colours: White shirts with Navy Blue shorts
Telephone Nº: 07946 388739
Social Club Phone Nº: (01943) 872872
Fax Number: (01943) 873223
Ground Capacity: 3,000
Seating Capacity: 518
Web site: www.guiseleyafc.co.uk
E-mail: admin@guiseleyafc.co.uk

GENERAL INFORMATION

Car Parking: At the ground and in Netherfield Road
Coach Parking: At the ground
Nearest Railway Station: Guiseley (5 minute walk)
Nearest Bus Station: Bus Stop outside the ground
Club Shop: At the ground
Opening Times: Matchdays only
Telephone Nº: (01943) 879236 (weekdays)
Postal Sales: Yes

GROUND INFORMATION

Away Supporters' Entrances & Sections:
No usual segregation

ADMISSION INFO (2016/2017 PRICES)

Adult Standing: £15.00
Adult Seating: £15.00
Ages 12 to 16 Standing/Seating: £5.00
Under-12s Standing/Seating: Free of charge when accompanied by a paying adult
Concessionary Standing/Seating: £10.00

DISABLED INFORMATION

Wheelchairs: Accommodated by the Players' Entrance
Helpers: Admitted
Prices: Free for both disabled fans and helpers
Disabled Toilets: None
Contact: (01943) 879236 (Bookings are advisable)

Travelling Supporters' Information:
Routes: Exit the M62 at Junction 28 and take the Leeds Ring Road to the roundabout at the junction of the A65 at Horsforth. Turn left onto the A65 and pass through Rawdon to Guiseley keeping Morrison's supermarket on your left. Pass straight through the traffic lights with the Station pub or your right and the ground is on the right after ¼ mile, adjacent to the cricket field.

LINCOLN CITY FC

Founded: 1884
Nickname: 'Red Imps'
Ground: Sincil Bank Stadium, Lincoln   LN5 8LD
Ground Capacity: 10,120 (All seats)
Record Attendance: 23,196 (15th November 1967)
Pitch Size: 110 × 72 yards

Colours: Red and White striped shirts, Black shorts
Telephone Nº: (01522) 880011
Ticket Office: (01522) 880011
Fax Number: (01522) 880020
Web Site: www.redimps.co.uk

GENERAL INFORMATION

Car Parking: Stacey West Car Park (limited parking for £5.00 per car).
Coach Parking: Please contact the club for details.
Nearest Railway Station: Lincoln Central
Club Shop: At the ground
Opening Times: Weekdays 10.00am to 2.00pm and Saturday Matchdays 10.00am until kick-off and 30 minutes after the final whistle
Telephone Nº: (01522) 880011

GROUND INFORMATION

Away Supporters' Entrances & Sections:
Lincolnshire Co-operative Stand (seated) – Turnstiles 24 & 25

ADMISSION INFO (2016/2017 PRICES)

Adult Seating: £18.00
Junior Seating: £7.00
Concessionary Seating: £13.00
Note: Discounts are available for families and for advance ticket purchases

DISABLED INFORMATION

Wheelchairs: Limited number of spaces available in the disabled section, adjacent to turnstile 23
Helpers: One helper admitted per disabled person
Prices: Applications for disabled passes must be made to the club. Wheelchair-bound disabled are charged concessionary prices. Helpers are admitted free if the disabled fan has a medium/high level disability allowance
Disabled Toilets: Adjacent to disabled area
Contact: (01522) 880011   (Bookings are necessary)

Travelling Supporters' Information:
Routes: From the East: Take the A46 or A158 into the City Centre following Newark (A46) signs into the High Street and take next left (Scorer Street and Cross Street) for the ground; From the North and West: Take the A15 or A57 into the City Centre, then as from the East; From the South: Take the A1 then A46 for the City Centre, then into the High Street, parking on the South Common or in the Stadium via South Park Avenue, turn down by the Fire Station.

MACCLESFIELD TOWN FC

Founded: 1874
Former Names: Macclesfield FC
Nickname: 'The Silkmen'
Ground: Moss Rose Ground, London Road, Macclesfield, Cheshire   SK11 7SP
Ground Capacity: 5,977
Seating Capacity: 2,599
Record Attendance: 10,041 (1948)

Pitch Size: 105 × 66 yards
Colours: Blue shirts, White shorts and Blue socks
Telephone Nº: (01625) 264686
Ticket Office: (01625) 264686
Fax Number: (01625) 264692
Web Site: www.mtfc.co.uk
E-mail: office@mtfc.co.uk

GENERAL INFORMATION

Car Parking: Ample parking available near the ground
Coach Parking: Near the ground
Nearest Railway Station: Macclesfield (1 mile)
Nearest Bus Station: Macclesfield
Club Shop: At the ground
Opening Times: Weekdays and matchdays 9.00am to 5.00pm
Telephone Nº: (01625) 264686

GROUND INFORMATION

Away Supporters' Entrances & Sections:
John Askey Terrace and the left side of the Moss Lane Stand

ADMISSION INFO (2016/2017 PRICES)

Adult Standing: £15.00
Adult Seating: £19.00
Concessions Standing: £10.00
Concessions Seating: £15.00
Under-12s Standing: £3.00
Under-12s Seating: £3.00
Under-18s/Student Standing: £5.00
Under-18s/Student Seating: £5.00

DISABLED INFORMATION

Wheelchairs: 45 spaces in front of the Estate Road Stand
Helpers: One helper admitted per disabled fan
Prices: Normal prices apply for the disabled. Helpers are admitted free of charge
Disabled Toilets: 3 available
Contact: (01625) 264686   (Bookings are necessary)

Travelling Supporters' Information:
Routes: From the North: Exit the M6 at Junction 19 to Knutsford, follow the A537 to Macclesfield. Follow signs for the Town Centre, then for the A523 to Leek. The ground is 1 mile out of the Town Centre on the right; From the South: Exit the M6 at Junction 17 for Sandbach and follow the A534 to Congleton. Then take the A536 to Macclesfield. After passing The Rising Sun on the left, turn right into Moss Lane after approximately ¼ mile . Following this lane will take you to the ground.

MAIDSTONE UNITED FC

Founded: 1992 (Reformed)
Former Names: Maidstone Invicta FC
Nickname: 'The Stones'
Ground: Gallagher Stadium, James Whatman Way, Maidstone ME14 1LQ
Record Attendance: 3,030 (5th April 2016)

Colours: Amber shirts with Black shorts
Telephone Nº: (01622) 753817
Ground Capacity: 3,030
Seating Capacity: 818
Web Site: www.maidstoneunited.co.uk

GENERAL INFORMATION

Car Parking: Various Pay & Display Car Parks available near the ground
Coach Parking: Maidstone coach park (1¼ miles) – please contact the club for further information
Nearest Railway Station: Maidstone East (¼ mile)
Club Shop: Available at the ground
Opening Times: Saturday Matchdays 12.30pm to 5.00pm; Tuesday Matchdays 6.15pm to 9.30pm.
Telephone Nº: (01622) 753817

GROUND INFORMATION

Away Supporters' Entrances & Sections:
No usual segregation – use the main turnstiles unless otherwise advertised.

ADMISSION INFO (2016/2017 PRICES)

Adult Standing: £15.00
Adult Seating: £17.00
Senior Citizen/Student Standing: £2.00
Senior Citizen/Student Seating: £14.00
Ages 11 to 16 Standing: £7.00
Ages 11 to 16 Seating: £9.00
Under-11s Standing: £2.00
Under-11s Seating: £4.00
Programme Price: £2.50

DISABLED INFORMATION

Wheelchairs: Accommodated
Helpers: Admitted
Prices: Normal prices apply for the disabled. Free for helpers
Disabled Toilets: Available
Contact: (01622) 753817 (Bookings are essential)

Travelling Supporters' Information:
Routes: Exit the M20 at Junction 6 or the M2 at Junction 3 and follow the A229 into Maidstone. After entering Maidstone, at the second roundabout (by the White Rabbit pub), take the third exit into James Whatman Way for the stadium.

NORTH FERRIBY UNITED FC

Founded: 1934
Former Names: None
Nickname: 'Villagers' or 'Green & Whites'
Ground: Eon Visual Media Stadium, Church Road, North Ferriby, East Yorkshire HU14 3AB
Record Attendance: 2,232 (vs Hull City in 2013)
Pitch Size: 109 × 76 yards

Colours: White shirts with Green trim, Green shorts
Telephone Nº: (01482) 634601
Fax Number: (01482) 634601
Ground Capacity: 3,000
Seating Capacity: 500
Web site: www.northferribyunited.com
E-mail: info@northferribyunitedfc.co.uk

GENERAL INFORMATION

Car Parking: Limited spaces at the ground
Coach Parking: At the ground
Nearest Railway Station: Ferriby (5 minutes walk)
Nearest Bus Station: Hull
Club Shop: At the ground
Opening Times: Matchdays only
Telephone Nº: (01482) 634601

GROUND INFORMATION

Away Supporters' Entrances & Sections:
No usual segregation

ADMISSION INFO (2016/2017 PRICES)

Adult Standing/Seating: £15.00
Senior Citizen Standing/Seating: £8.00
Under-16s Standing/Seating: £4.00
Note: Under-12s are admitted free of charge when accompanied by a paying adult.
Programme Price: £2.00

DISABLED INFORMATION

Wheelchairs: Accommodated
Helpers: Admitted
Prices: Standard prices apply
Disabled Toilets: Available
Contact: (01482) 634601 (Bookings are not necessary)

Travelling Supporters' Information:
Routes: North Ferriby is approximately 8 miles to the west of Hull on the A63. Upon reaching North Ferriby (from the West), proceed through the village past the Duke of Cumberland Hotel and turn right into Church Lane. The ground is situated on the left after half a mile.

SOLIHULL MOORS FC

Photo courtesy of Jordan Martin Photography

Founded: 2007
Former Names: Formed by the merger of Solihull Borough FC and Moor Green FC in 2007
Nickname: 'The Moors'
Ground: The Autotech Stadium, Damson Park, Damson Parkway, Solihull B91 2PP
Record Attendance: 1,912 (vs Birmingham City)
Pitch Size: 114 × 76 yards

Colours: Yellow and Blue hooped shirts, Blue shorts
Telephone Nº: (0121) 705-6770
Fax Number: (0121) 711-4045
Ground Capacity: 3,300
Seating Capacity: 500
Web site: www.solihullmoorsfc.co.uk
E-mail: solihullfootball@btconnect.com

GENERAL INFORMATION
Car Parking: At the ground
Coach Parking: At the ground
Nearest Railway Station: Birmingham International (2 miles)
Nearest Bus Station: Birmingham (5 miles)
Club Shop: At the ground
Opening Times: Matchdays only
Telephone Nº: (0121) 705-6770

GROUND INFORMATION
Away Supporters' Entrances & Sections:
No usual segregation

ADMISSION INFO (2016/2017 PRICES)
Adult Standing: £14.00
Adult Seating: £14.00
Senior Citizen/Junior Standing: £8.00
Senior Citizen/Junior Seating: £8.00
Note: Under-12s are admitted free of charge when accompanied by a paying adult

DISABLED INFORMATION
Wheelchairs: Spaces for 3 wheelchairs are available
Helpers: Admitted
Prices: Normal prices apply
Disabled Toilets: Available
Contact: (0121) 705-6770

Travelling Supporters' Information:
Routes: Exit the M42 at Junction 6 and take the A45 for 2 miles towards Birmingham. Turn left at the traffic lights near the Posthouse Hotel into Damson Parkway (signposted for Landrover/Damsonwood). Continue to the roundabout and come back along the other carriageway to the ground which is situated on the left after about 150 yards.

SOUTHPORT FC

Founded: 1881
Former Names: Southport Vulcan FC, Southport Central FC
Nickname: 'The Sandgrounders' and 'The Port'
Ground: Merseyrail Community Stadium, Haig Avenue, Southport, Merseyside   PR8 6JZ
Record Attendance: 20,010 (1932)
Pitch Size: 110 × 77 yards

Colours: Yellow shirts and shorts
Telephone Nº: (01704) 533422
Fax Number: (01704) 533455
Ground Capacity: 6,008
Seating Capacity: 1,660
Web site: www.southportfc.net

GENERAL INFORMATION

Car Parking: Street parking
Coach Parking: Adjacent to the ground
Nearest Railway Station: Meols Cop (½ mile)
Nearest Bus Station: Southport Town Centre
Club Shop: At the ground
Opening Times: Matchdays from 1.30pm (from 6.30pm on evening matchdays)
Telephone Nº: (01704) 533422

GROUND INFORMATION

Away Supporters' Entrances & Sections:
Blowick End entrances

ADMISSION INFO (2016/2017 PRICES)

Adult Standing: £13.50
Adult Seating: £15.00
Concessionary Standing: £10.00
Concessionary Seating: £11.00
Under-19s Standing/Seating: £5.00
Note: Children aged 11 and under are admitted free of charge when accompanied by a paying adult.

DISABLED INFORMATION

Wheelchairs: Accommodated in front of the Grandstand
Helpers: Admitted
Prices: Concessionary prices charged for the disabled. Helpers are admitted free of charge
Disabled Toilets: Available at the Blowick End of the Grandstand
Contact: (01704) 533422   (Bookings are not necessary)

Travelling Supporters' Information:
Routes: Exit the M58 at Junction 3 and take the A570 to Southport. At the major roundabout (McDonalds/Tesco) go straight on into Scarisbrick New Road, pass over the brook and turn right into Haig Avenue at the traffic lights. The ground is then on the right-hand side.

SUTTON UNITED FC

Founded: 1898
Former Names: Formed by the amalgamation of Sutton Guild Rovers FC and Sutton Association FC
Nickname: 'U's'
Ground: Borough Sports Ground, Gander Green Lane, Sutton, Surrey SM1 2EY
Record Attendance: 14,000 (1970)

Colours: Shirts are Amber with a Chocolate pin-stripe, Amber shorts
Telephone Nº: (020) 8644-4440
Fax Number: (020) 8644-5120
Ground Capacity: 5,013
Seating Capacity: 765
Web site: www.suttonunited.net

GENERAL INFORMATION

Car Parking: 150 spaces behind the Main Stand
Coach Parking: Space for 1 coach in the car park
Nearest Railway Station: West Sutton (adjacent)
Club Shop: At the ground
Opening Times: Matchdays only
Telephone Nº: (020) 8644-4440

GROUND INFORMATION

Away Supporters' Entrances & Sections:
Collingwood Road entrances and accommodation

ADMISSION INFO (2016/2017 PRICES)

Adult Standing: £15.00
Adult Seating: £17.00
Child Standing: £3.00
Child Seating: £5.00
Senior Citizen Standing: £8.00
Senior Citizen Seating: £10.00

DISABLED INFORMATION

Wheelchairs: 8 spaces are available under cover accommodated on the track perimeter
Helpers: Admitted
Prices: Normal prices apply
Disabled Toilets: Available alongside the Standing Terrace
Contact: (020) 8644-4440 (Bookings are necessary)

Travelling Supporters' Information:
Routes: Exit the M25 at Junction 8 (Reigate Hill) and travel North on the A217 for approximately 8 miles. Cross the A232 then turn right at the traffic lights (past Goose & Granit Public House) into Gander Green Lane. The ground is 300 yards on the left; From London: Gander Green Lane crosses the Sutton bypass 1 mile south of Rose Hill Roundabout. Avoid Sutton Town Centre, especially on Saturdays.

TORQUAY UNITED FC

Founded: 1899
Former Name: Torquay Town FC (1899-1910)
Nickname: 'Gulls'
Ground: Plainmoor Ground, Torquay   TQ1 3PS
Ground Capacity: 6,200   **Seating Capacity**: 2,841
Record Attendance: 21,908 (29th January 1955)
Pitch Size: 112 × 72 yards

Colours: Yellow shirts and Blue shorts
Telephone Nº: (01803) 328666
Ticket Office: (01803) 328666
Fax Number: (01803) 323976
Web Site: www.torquayunited.com
E-mail: reception@torquayunited.com

GENERAL INFORMATION

Car Parking: Street parking
Coach Parking: Lymington Road Coach Station (½ mile)
Nearest Railway Station: Torquay (2 miles)
Nearest Bus Station: Lymington Road (½ mile)
Club Shop: At the ground
Opening Times: Matchdays and during Office Hours
Telephone Nº: (01803) 328666

GROUND INFORMATION

Away Supporters' Entrances & Sections:
Babbacombe End turnstiles for Babbacombe End

ADMISSION INFO (2016/2017 PRICES)

Adult Standing: £15.00
Adult Seating: £17.00 – £19.00
Concessionary Standing: £12.00
Concessionary Seating: £14.00 – £15.00
Under-18s Standing/Seating: £7.00
Note: Family tickets are also available
Programme Price: £3.00

DISABLED INFORMATION

Wheelchairs: 9 spaces in front of Bristow Bench Stand for home supporters plus 9 spaces in the Away end.
Helpers: One helper admitted per wheelchair
Prices: Normal prices for the disabled. Free for helpers
Disabled Toilets: Available in the Ellacombe End and the Away End
Contact: (01803) 328666   (Bookings are not necessary)

Travelling Supporters' Information:
Routes: From the North and East: Take the M5 to the A38 then A380 to Torquay. On entering Torquay, turn left at the 1st set of traffic lights after Riviera Way Retail Park into Hele Road. Following signs for the ground, continue straight on over two mini-roundabouts, go up West Hill Road to the traffic lights, then straight ahead into Warbro Road. The ground is situated on the right after 200 yards.

TRANMERE ROVERS FC

Founded: 1884
Former Name: Belmont FC
Nickname: 'Rovers'
Ground: Prenton Park, Prenton Road West, Birkenhead   CH42 9PY
Ground Capacity: 16,151 (All seats)
Record Attendance: 24,424 (5th February 1972)

Pitch Size: 110 × 70 yards
Colours: White shirts and shorts
Telephone Nº: 03330 144452
Ticket Office: 03330 144452
Fax Number: (0151) 609-0606
Web Site: www.tranmererovers.co.uk
E-mail: customerservice@tranmererovers.co.uk

GENERAL INFORMATION

Car Parking: Large car park at the ground (£5.00 per car)
Coach Parking: At the ground (£10.00 charge)
Nearest Railway Stations: Hamilton Square, Rock Ferry and Conway Park (approximately 1½ miles)
Nearest Bus Station: Conway Park (Town Centre)
Club Shop: At the ground
Opening Times: Weekdays 9.30am–5.00pm, Matchdays 10.00am–kick-off, non-Saturday matchdays 10.00am–1.00pm
Telephone Nº: 03330 144452

GROUND INFORMATION

Away Supporters' Entrances & Sections:
Cowshed Stand turnstiles 5-9 – access from Borough Road (Away section capacity: 2,500)

ADMISSION INFO (2016/2017 PRICES)

Adult Seating: £17.00 – £20.00
Under-12s Seating: £2.00 – £5.00
Under-17s Seating: £5.00 – £6.00
Senior Citizen Seating: £10.00 – £13.00
Young Persons Ticket (Ages 17-22): £10.00 – £13.00
Programme Price: £3.00
Note: Young Person tickets must be purchased from the Ticket Office prior to the game and are only sold upon presentation of photographic proof of age.

DISABLED INFORMATION

Wheelchairs: 40 spaces in total for Home and Away fans in the disabled section, Bebington Paddock
Helpers: One helper admitted per disabled person
Prices: £8.00
Disabled Toilets: 2 available in the disabled section
Contact: 03330 144452 (Bookings are necessary)

Travelling Supporters' Information:
Routes: From the North: From Liverpool city centre, travel through the Kingsway (Wallasey) Mersey Tunnel (£1.70 toll for cars) then continue onto the M53, exiting at Junction 3. Take the first exit (signposted Birkenhead), continue past Sainsbury's then turn right at the traffic lights by the Halfway House pub then turn left into Prenton Road West at the next set of lights. The ground is on the right after a short distance. From the South: Exit the M53 at Junction 4 and take the 4th exit at the roundabout onto the B5151 Mount Road (the ground is signposted from here). After 2½ miles, turn right at the traffic lights (by the United Reformed Church) into Prenton Road West for the ground.

WOKING FC

Founded: 1889
Former Names: None
Nickname: 'Cardinals'
Ground: Laithwaite Community Stadium, Kingfield, Woking, Surrey   GU22 9AA
Record Attendance: 6,000 (1997)
Pitch Size: 109 × 76 yards

Colours: Shirts are Red & White halves, Black shorts
Telephone Nº: (01483) 772470
Daytime Phone Nº: (01483) 772470
Fax Number: (01483) 888423
Ground Capacity: 6,161
Seating Capacity: 2,511
Web site: www.wokingfc.co.uk
E-mail: admin@wokingfc.co.uk

GENERAL INFORMATION

Car Parking: Limited parking at the ground
Coach Parking: Please contact the club for details
Nearest Railway Station: Woking (1 mile)
Nearest Bus Station: Woking
Club Shop: At the ground
Opening Times: Weekdays 10.00am to 3.00pm and Matchdays 1.00pm to 3.00pm.
Telephone Nº: (01483) 772470

GROUND INFORMATION

Away Supporters' Entrances & Sections:
Kingfield Road entrance for the Tennis Club terrace

ADMISSION INFO (2016/2017 PRICES)

Adult Standing: £18.00
Adult Seating: £18.00
Under-16s/Student Standing: £5.00
Under-16s/Student Seating: £5.00
Senior Citizen Standing: £13.00
Senior Citizen Seating: £13.00

DISABLED INFORMATION

Wheelchairs: 8 spaces in the Leslie Gosden Stand and 8 spaces in front of the Family Stand
Helpers: Admitted
Prices: One wheelchair and helper for £13.00
Disabled Toilets: Yes – in the Leslie Gosden Stand and Family Stand area
Contact: (01483) 772470   (Bookings are necessary)

Travelling Supporters' Information:
Routes: Exit the M25 at Junction 10 and follow the A3 towards Guildford. Leave at the next junction onto the B2215 through Ripley and join the A247 to Woking. Alternatively, exit the M25 at Junction 11 and follow the A320 to Woking Town Centre. The ground is on the outskirts of Woking – follow signs on the A320 and A247.

WREXHAM AFC

Founded: 1864
Nickname: 'Red Dragons'
Ground: Racecourse Ground, Mold Road, Wrexham, North Wales   LL11 2AH
Ground Capacity: 10,500 (all seats)
Record Attendance: 34,445 (26th January 1957)
Pitch Size: 111 × 71 yards

Colours: Red shirts with White shorts
Telephone Nº: (01978) 891864
Web Site: www.wrexhamafc.co.uk
E-mail: info@wrexhamfc.tv

GENERAL INFORMATION
Car Parking: Town car parks are nearby and also Glyndwr University (Mold End)
Coach Parking: By Police direction
Nearest Railway Station: Wrexham General (adjacent)
Nearest Bus Station: Wrexham (King Street)
Club Shop: At the ground in the Yale Stand
Opening Times: Monday to Friday 10.00am to 5.00pm
Telephone Nº: (01978) 891864

GROUND INFORMATION
Away Supporters' Entrances & Sections:
Turnstiles 1-4 for the Yale Stand

ADMISSION INFO (2016/2017 PRICES)
Adult Seating: £16.00 – £20.00
Under-16s Seating: £7.00 – £8.00
Under-11s Seating: £1.00 (with a paying adult)
Concessionary Seating: £13.00 – £14.00
Over-80s Seating: £7.00 – £8.00
Note: Discounts apply for advance purchases and Family tickets are also available

DISABLED INFORMATION
Wheelchairs: 35 spaces in the Mold Road Stand
Helpers: One helper admitted per wheelchair
Prices: Normal prices for the disabled. Free for helpers
Disabled Toilets: Available in the disabled section
Contact: (01978) 262129   (Diann Mitchell)

Travelling Supporters' Information:
Routes: From the North and West: Take the A483 and the Wrexham bypass to the junction with the A541. Branch left at the roundabout and follow Wrexham signs into Mold Road; From the East: Take the A525 or A534 into Wrexham then follow the A541 signs into Mold Road; From the South: Take the the M6, then the M54 and follow the A5 and A483 to the Wrexham bypass and the junction with the A541. Branch right at the roundabout and follow signs for the Town Centre.

YORK CITY FC |

Founded: 1922	**Colours**: Red shirts with Blue shorts
Nickname: 'The Minstermen'	**Telephone Nº**: (01904) 559503
Ground: Bootham Crescent, York YO30 7AQ	**Ticket Office**: (01904) 559503 Extension 1
Ground Capacity: 8,105	**Fax Number**: (01904) 631457
Seating Capacity: 3,509	**Web Site**: www.yorkcityfootballclub.co.uk
Record Attendance: 28,123 (5th March 1938)	**E-mail**: enquiries@yorkcityfootballclub.co.uk
Pitch Size: 115 × 74 yards	

GENERAL INFORMATION

Car Parking: Street parking
Coach Parking: By Police direction
Nearest Railway Station: York (1 mile)
Club Shop: At the ground
Opening Times: Weekdays 12.00am – 5.00pm;
Saturday Matchdays 1.00pm–3.00pm and 4.40pm–5.30pm;
Evening matches open from 6.00pm
Telephone Nº: (01904) 624447 Extension 4

GROUND INFORMATION

Away Supporters' Entrances & Sections:
Grosvenor Road turnstiles for Grosvenor Road End

ADMISSION INFO (2016/2017 PRICES)

Adult Standing: £18.00
Adult Seating: £19.00 – £21.00
Concessionary Standing: £12.00
Concessionary Seating: £13.00 – £14.00
Under-16s Standing/Seating: £12.00 – £14.00
Programme Price: £3.00

DISABLED INFORMATION

Wheelchairs: 18 spaces in total for Home and Away fans in
the disabled section, in front of the Pitchside Bar
Helpers: One helper admitted per disabled person
Prices: £12.00 – £18.00 for the disabled. Helpers are
admitted free of charge
Disabled Toilets: Available at entrance to the disabled area
Contact: (01904) 624447 (Ext. 1) (Bookings not necessary)

Travelling Supporters' Information:
Routes: From the North: Take the A1 then the A59 following signs for York. Cross the railway bridge and turn left after 2 miles into Water End. Turn right at the end following City Centre signs for nearly ½ mile then turn left into Bootham Crescent; From the South: Take the A64 and turn left after Buckles Inn onto the Outer Ring Road. Turn right onto the A19, follow City Centre signs for 1½ miles then turn left into Bootham Crescent; From the East: Take the Outer Ring Road turning left onto the A19. Then as from the South; From the West: Take the Outer Ring Road turning right onto the A19. Then as from the South.

THE VANARAMA NATIONAL LEAGUE NORTH

Address

4th Floor, 20 Waterloo Street,
Birmingham   B2 5TB

Phone (0121) 643-3143

Web site   www.footballconference.co.uk

Clubs for the 2016/2017 Season

AFC Fylde .... Page 31
AFC Telford United .... Page 32
Alfreton Town FC .... Page 33
Altrincham FC .... Page 34
Boston United FC .... Page 35
Brackley Town FC .... Page 36
Bradford Park Avenue FC .... Page 37
Chorley FC .... Page 38
Curzon Ashton FC .... Page 39
Darlington 1883 .... Page 40
FC Halifax Town .... Page 41
FC United of Manchester .... Page 42
Gainsborough Trinity FC .... Page 43
Gloucester City FC .... Page 44
Harrogate Town FC .... Page 45
Kidderminster Harriers FC .... Page 46
Nuneaton Town FC .... Page 47
Salford City FC .... Page 48
Stalybridge Celtic FC .... Page 49
Stockport County FC .... Page 50
Tamworth FC .... Page 51
Worcester City FC .... Page 52

AFC FYLDE

Photo courtesy of John Mills @ Altius Photography

Founded: 1988
Former Names: Formed by the amalgamation of Wesham FC and Kirkham Town FC in 1988
Nickname: 'The Coasters'
Ground: Mill Farm, Coronation Way, Wesham, Preston PR4 3JZ
Record Attendance: Not applicable

Colours: White shirts and shorts
Telephone Nº: (01772) 682593
Fax Number: (01772) 685893
Ground Capacity: 6,000
Seating Capacity: 2,000
Pitch Size: 110 × 72 yards
Web Site: www.afcfylde.co.uk

GENERAL INFORMATION

Car Parking: At the ground
Coach Parking: At the ground
Nearest Railway Station: Kirkham & Wesham (1 mile)
Club Shop: 6 Station Road, Kirkham PR4 2AS
Opening Times: Monday to Thursday 9.00am to 12.00pm and Fridays a& Saturdays 9.00am to 1.00pm
Telephone Nº: (01772) 682593 (Phone orders accepted)

GROUND INFORMATION

Away Supporters' Entrances & Sections:
No usual segregation

ADMISSION INFO (2016/2017 PRICES)

Adult Standing: £12.00
Adult Seating: £15.00
Concessionary Standing: £9.00
Concessionary Seating: £9.00
Student Standing: £5.00
Student Seating: £5.00
Under-16s Standing: £5.00 (Free of charge for members)
Under-16s Seating: £8.00 (Free of charge for members)
Programme Price: £2.00

DISABLED INFORMATION

Wheelchairs: Accommodated
Helpers: Admitted
Prices: Normal prices apply for the disabled. Helpers pay concessionary prices
Disabled Toilets: Available
Contact: (01772) 682593 (Bookings are not necessary)

Travelling Supporters' Information:
Routes: The Mill Farm Sports Village is situated by the side of the A585, just to the north of Wesham and less than a mile to the south of Junction 3 of the M55.

AFC TELFORD UNITED

Founded: 2004
Former Names: Formed after Telford United FC went out of business. TUFC were previously known as Wellington Town FC
Nickname: 'The Bucks'
Ground: The New Bucks Head Stadium, Watling Street, Wellington, Telford   TF1 2TU
Record Attendance: 13,000 (1935)

Pitch Size: 110 × 74 yards
Colours: White shirts and shorts
Telehone Nº: (01952) 640064
Fax Number: (01952) 640021
Ground Capacity: 5,780
Seating Capacity: 2,280
Web site: www.telfordunited.com
E-mail: office@telfordutd.co.uk

GENERAL INFORMATION

Car Parking: At the ground (£3.00 charge for cars)
Coach Parking: At the ground
Nearest Railway Station: Wellington
Nearest Bus Station: Wellington
Club Shop: At the ground
Opening Times: Saturday matchdays only from 1.30pm.
Telephone Nº: None

GROUND INFORMATION

Away Supporters' Entrances & Sections:
Frank Nagington Stand on the rare occasions when segregation is used

ADMISSION INFO (2016/2017 PRICES)

Adult Standing: £14.00
Adult Seating: £14.00
Under-16s Standing: £3.00
Under-16s Seating: £3.00
Under-20s Standing: £5.00
Under-20s Seating: £5.00
Concessionary Standing: £10.00
Concessionary Seating: £10.00

DISABLED INFORMATION

Wheelchairs: Accommodated at both ends of the ground
Helpers: Admitted
Prices: Normal prices apply
Disabled Toilets: Available by the Sir Stephen Roberts Stand
Contact: (01952) 640064   (Bookings are not necessary)

Travelling Supporters' Information:
Routes: Exit the M54 at Junction 6 and take the A518. Go straight on at the first roundabout, take the second exit at the next roundabout then turn left at the following roundabout. Follow the road round to the right then turn left into the car park.

ALFRETON TOWN FC

Founded: 1959
Former Names: None
Nickname: 'Reds'
Ground: The Impact Arena, North Street, Alfreton, Derbyshire   DE55 7FZ
Record Attendance: 5,023 vs Matlock Town (1960)
Pitch Size: 110 × 75 yards

Colours: Red shirts and shorts
Telephone Nº: (0115) 939-2090
Fax Number: (0115) 949-1846
Ground Capacity: 5,100
Seating Capacity: 1,600
Web site: www.alfretontownfc.com

GENERAL INFORMATION

Car Parking: At the ground
Coach Parking: Available close to the ground
Nearest Railway Station: Alfreton (½ mile)
Nearest Bus Station: Alfreton (5 minutes walk)
Club Shop: At the ground
Opening Times: Matchdays only
Telephone Nº: (01773) 830277

GROUND INFORMATION

Away Supporters' Entrances & Sections:
Segregation is usual so please check prior to the game

ADMISSION INFO (2016/2017 PRICES)

Adult Standing: £14.00
Adult Seating: £14.00
Senior Citizen Standing/Seating: £10.00
Ages 16 to 21 Standing/Seating: £10.00
Under-16s Standing: £2.00 (with a paying adult)
Under-16s Seating: £2.00 (with a paying adult)

DISABLED INFORMATION

Wheelchairs: Accommodated in dedicated areas of the ground
Helpers: Admitted
Prices: Please phone the club for information
Disabled Toilets: Available
Contact: (01773) 830277   (Bookings are not necessary)

Travelling Supporters' Information:
Routes: Exit the M1 at Junction 28 and take the A38 signposted for Derby. After 2 miles take the sliproad onto the B600 then go right at the main road towards the town centre. After ½ mile turn left down North Street and the ground is on the right after 200 yards.

ALTRINCHAM FC

Founded: 1891
Former Names: Broadheath FC
Nickname: 'The Robins'
Ground: The J. Davidson Stadium, Moss Lane, Altrincham WA15 8AP
Record Attendance: 10,275 (February 1925)
Pitch Size: 110 × 72 yards
Web site: www.altrinchamfc.com

Colours: Red and White striped shirts, Black shorts
Telephone Nº: (0161) 928-1045
Daytime Phone Nº: (0161) 928-1045
Fax Number: (0161) 926-9934
Ground Capacity: 6,085
Seating Capacity: 1,154
E-mail: office@altrinchamfootballclub.co.uk

GENERAL INFORMATION

Car Parking: Limited street parking
Coach Parking: By Police Direction
Nearest Railway Station: Altrincham (15 minutes walk)
Nearest Bus Station: Altrincham
Club Shop: Inside the ground
Opening Times: Matchdays only. Opens one hour prior to the start of the game.
Telephone Nº: (0161) 928-1045

GROUND INFORMATION

Away Supporters' Entrances & Sections:
Hale End turnstiles and accommodation

ADMISSION INFO (2016/2017 PRICES)

Adult Standing: £14.00
Adult Seating: £15.00
Concessionary Standing: £9.00
Concessionary Seating: £10.00
Ages 12-16 years Standing/Seating: £5.00
Under-12s Standing/Seating: £2.00

DISABLED INFORMATION

Wheelchairs: 3 spaces are available each for home and away fans adjacent to the Away dugout
Helpers: Admitted
Prices: £14.00 combined price for a disabled fan and helper
Disabled Toilets: Yes
Contact: (0161) 928-1045 (Bookings are necessary)

Travelling Supporters' Information:
Routes: Exit the M56 at either Junction 6 or 7 and follow the signs for Altrincham FC.

BOSTON UNITED FC

Founded: 1933
Former Names: Boston Town FC & Boston Swifts FC
Nickname: 'The Pilgrims'
Ground: Jakemans Stadium, York Street, Boston, PE21 6JN
Ground Capacity: 6,613 **Seating Capacity**: 2,000
Pitch Size: 112 × 72 yards
Record Attendance: 10,086 (1955)

Colours: Amber and Black shirts with Black shorts and Amber socks
Telephone Nº: (01205) 364406 (Office)
Matchday Info: (01205) 364406 or 07860 663299
Fax Number: (01205) 354063
Web Site: www.bufc.co.uk
E-mail: admin@bufc.co.uk

GENERAL INFORMATION

Car Parking: Permit holders only
Coach Parking: Available near to the ground
Nearest Railway Station: Boston (1 mile)
Nearest Bus Station: Boston Coach Station (¼ mile)
Club Shop: In the car park at the ground
Opening Times: Weekdays from 9.00am to 5.00pm and Saturday Matchdays from 11.00am to 5.00pm
Telephone Nº: (01205) 364406

GROUND INFORMATION

Away Supporters' Entrances & Sections:
York Street Entrances 3 & 4 (subject to a move to the Jakemans Stand if so advised by the police)

ADMISSION INFO (2016/2017 PRICES)

Adult Standing: £13.00
Adult Seating: £15.00
Child Standing: £4.00
Child Seating: £5.00
Senior Citizen Standing: £10.00
Senior Citizen Seating: £11.00

DISABLED INFORMATION

Wheelchairs: 7 spaces available for home fans, 4 spaces for away fans below the Main Stand at the Town End
Helpers: One helper admitted per disabled fan
Prices: £13.00 for the disabled. Free of charge for helpers
Disabled Toilets: Available in the Town End Terrace
Contact: (01205) 364406 (Bookings are necessary)

Travelling Supporters' Information:
From the North: Take the A17 from Sleaford, bear right after the railway crossing to the traffic lights over the bridge. Go forward through the traffic lights into York Street for the ground; From the South: Take the A16 from Spalding and turn right at the traffic lights over the bridge. Go forward through the next traffic lights into York Street for the ground.

BRACKLEY TOWN FC

Founded: 1890
Former Names: None
Nickname: 'Saints'
Ground: St. James Park, Churchill Way, Brackley, NN13 7EJ
Record Attendance: 2,604 (2012/13 season)

Colours: Red and Black striped shirts with Black shorts
Telephone Nº: (01280) 704077
Ground Capacity: 3,500
Seating Capacity: 300
Web Site: www.brackleytownfc.com

GENERAL INFORMATION

Car Parking: At the ground (£2.00 charge per car)
Coach Parking: At the ground
Nearest Railway Station: King's Sutton (6¾ miles)
Club Shop: At the ground
Opening Times: Matchdays and by appointment only
Telephone Nº: (01280) 704077

GROUND INFORMATION

Away Supporters' Entrances & Sections:
No usual segregation

ADMISSION INFO (2016/2017 PRICES)

Adult Standing: £12.00
Adult Seating: £12.00
Senior Citizen/Student Standing: £6.00
Senior Citizen/Student Seating: £6.00
Under-16s Standing: £3.00
Under-16s Seating: £3.00

DISABLED INFORMATION

Wheelchairs: Accommodated
Helpers: Admitted
Prices: Normal prices apply for the disabled and helpers
Disabled Toilets: Available
Contact: (01280) 704077 (Stephen Toghill – bookings are necessary)

Travelling Supporters' Information:
Routes: From the West: Take the A422 to Brackley and take the first exit at the roundabout with the junction of the A43, heading north into Oxford Road. * Go straight on at the next roundabout and continue into Bridge Street before turning right into Churchill Way. The ground is located at the end of the road; From the South: Take the A43 northwards to Brackley. Take the second exit at the roundabout with the junction of the A422 and head into Oxford Road. Then as from * above; From the North-East: Take the A43 to Brackley. Upon reaching Brackley, take the 1st exit at the 1st roundabout, the 2nd exit at the next roundabout then the 3rd exit at the following roundabout into Oxford Road. Then as from * above.

BRADFORD PARK AVENUE FC

Founded: 1907 (Re-formed in 1988)
Former Names: None
Nickname: 'Avenue'
Ground: Horsfall Stadium, Cemetery Road, Bradford, BD6 2NG
Record Attendance: 2,100 (2003)
Pitch Size: 112 × 71 yards

Colours: Green & White striped shirts, White shorts
Telephone Nº: 07912 271498 (Ground)
Office Address: Hugh House, Foundry Street, Brighouse HD6 1LT
Office Number: (01484) 400007
Ground Capacity: 3,000 **Seating Capacity**: 1,247
Web site: www.bpafc.com

GENERAL INFORMATION

Car Parking: Street parking and some spaces at the ground
Coach Parking: At the ground
Nearest Railway Station: Bradford Interchange (3 miles)
Nearest Bus Station: Bradford Interchange (3 miles)
Club Shop: At the ground
Opening Times: Matchdays only
Telephone Nº: –

GROUND INFORMATION

Away Supporters' Entrances & Sections:
Segregation only used when required

ADMISSION INFO (2016/2017 PRICES)

Adult Standing/Seating: £11.00
Senior Citizen Standing/Seating: £7.00
Student Standing/Seating: £7.00
Under-16s Standing/Seating: £2.00
Armed Forces Standing/Seating: £5.00 (warrant card must be shown)

DISABLED INFORMATION

Wheelchairs: Accommodated in front of the Stand
Helpers: Please phone the club for information
Prices: Please phone the club for information
Disabled Toilets: Available
Contact: – (Bookings are not necessary)

Travelling Supporters' Information:
Routes: Exit the M62 at Junction 26 and take the M606 to its end. At the roundabout go along the A6036 (signposted Halifax) and pass Odsal Stadium on the left. At the roundabout by Odsal take the 3rd exit (still A6036 Halifax). After just under 1 mile, turn left at the Kinderhaven Nursery into Cemetery Road. The ground is 150 yards on the left.

CHORLEY FC

Founded: 1883
Former Names: None
Nickname: 'Magpies'
Ground: The Chorley Group Victory Park Stadium, Duke Street, Chorley, PR7 3DU
Record Attendance: 9,679 (1931/32 season)
Pitch Size: 112 × 72 yards

Colours: Black & White striped shirts with Black shorts
Telephone Nº: (01257) 230007
Fax Number: (01257) 275662
Ground Capacity: 3,550
Seating Capacity: 900
Web site: www.chorleyfc.com
E-mail: info@chorleyfc.com

GENERAL INFORMATION
Car Parking: 80 spaces available at the ground (£3.00)
Coach Parking: At the ground
Nearest Railway Station: Chorley (¼ mile)
Nearest Bus Station: 15 minutes from the ground
Club Shop: At the ground
Opening Times: Matchdays only
Telephone Nº: –

GROUND INFORMATION
Away Supporters' Entrances & Sections:
Pilling Lane Stand entrances and accommodation

ADMISSION INFO (2016/2017 PRICES)
Adult Standing: £10.00
Adult Seating: £10.00
Concessionary Standing/Seating: £7.00
Under-16s Standing/Seating: £5.00
Under-12s Standing/Seating: £2.00
Under-8s Standing/Seating: Free of charge
Programme Price: £2.50

DISABLED INFORMATION
Wheelchairs: Accommodated by prior arrangement
Helpers: Please contact the club for information
Prices: Please contact the club for information
Disabled Toilets: Available in the Social Club
Contact: (01257) 230007 (Bookings are not necessary)

Travelling Supporters' Information:
Routes: Exit the M61 at Junction 6 and follow the A6 to Chorley. Going past the Yarrow Bridge Hotel on Bolton Road, turn left at the 1st set of traffic lights into Pilling Lane. Take the 1st right into Ashby Street and the ground is the 2nd entrance on the left; Alternative Route: Exit the M6 at Junction 27 and follow signs to Chorley. Turn left at the lights and continue down the A49 for 2½ miles before turning right onto B5251. On entering Chorley, turn right into Duke Street 200 yards past The Plough.

CURZON ASHTON FC

Founded: 1963
Former Names: None
Nickname: 'The Nash'
Ground: Tameside Stadium, Richmond Street, Ashton-under-Lyne   OL7 9HG
Record Attendance: 1,826
Pitch Size: 114 × 72 yards

Colours: Royal Blue shirts and shorts
Telephone Nº: (0161) 330-6033
Fax Number: (0161) 339-8802
Ground Capacity: 4,000
Seating Capacity: 527
Web Site: www.curzon-ashton.co.uk

GENERAL INFORMATION

Car Parking: At the ground
Coach Parking: At the ground
Nearest Railway Station: Ashton-under-Lyne (1 mile)
Club Shop: At the ground
Opening Times: Matchdays only
Telephone Nº: (0161) 330-6033

GROUND INFORMATION

Away Supporters' Entrances & Sections:
No usual segregation

ADMISSION INFO (2016/2017 PRICES)

Adult Standing: £10.00
Adult Seating: £10.00
Concessionary Standing: £5.00
Concessionary Seating: £5.00
Under-16s Standing: £3.00
Under-16s Seating: £3.00
Programme Price: £2.00

DISABLED INFORMATION

Wheelchairs: Accommodated
Helpers: Admitted
Prices: Normal prices apply for the disabled and helpers
Disabled Toilets: Available
Contact: (0161) 330-6033   (Bookings are not necessary)

Travelling Supporters' Information:
Routes: Exit the M60 at Junction 23 and take the A6140 signposted for Ashton. Continue along the A6140 to the set of traffic lights with a Cinema on the right then turn left. Cross over a bridge and go straight across the mini-roundabout before turning left into the ground. NOTE: Diversions may be in force during the 2010/2011 season due to bridge replacement work.

DARLINGTON 1883

Darlington 1883 hope to be able to play games back home in Darlington at some point during the 2016/2017 season and have entered into a groundsharing agreement with Darlington RFC to use their Blackwell Meadows ground. However, it is not yet known when matches at Blackwell Meadows will commence. Until that point, matches will be played at Bishop Auckland's Heritage Park and we would suggest that travelling fans contact the club or check the web site for further details.

Founded: 1883 (Re-formed 2012)
Former Names: Successor to the club Darlington FC
Nickname: 'Darlo', 'The Quakers'
Ground: Heritage Park, Bishop Auckland,
DL14 9AE
Record Attendance: 2,000 (April 2013)
Pitch Size: 110 × 75 yards

Ground Capacity: 2,000
Seating Capacity: 250
Colours: Black and White hooped shirts, Black shorts
Contact Telephone No: None
Web Site: www.darlingtonfootballclub.co.uk
E-mail: secretary@darlingtonfc.org

GENERAL INFORMATION
Car Parking: Limited parking at the ground
Coach Parking: Limited parking at the ground
Nearest Railway Station: Bishop Auckland (2 miles)
Nearest Bus Station: Darlington (12 miles)
Club Shop: Online sales only at present
Telephone No: 07717 345004

GROUND INFORMATION
Away Supporters' Entrances & Sections:
No usual segregation

ADMISSION INFO (2016/2017 PRICES)
Adult Standing: £10.00
Adult Seating: £12.00 (No seating for away supporters)
Over-60s Standing/Seating: £7.00
Junior Standing/Seating (Ages 5–16): £4.00
Programme Price: £2.50

DISABLED INFORMATION
Wheelchairs: Accommodated
Helpers: Helpers are admitted
Prices: Normal prices apply for the disabled and helpers
Disabled Toilets: Available
Contact: secretary@darlingtonfc.org (Bookings are not necessary)

Travelling Supporters' Information:
Routes: Darlington 1883 are currently groundsharing with Bishop Auckland Football Club at Heritage Park. Exit the A1(M) at Junction 58 and follow the A68 to West Auckland. Take the third exit at the roundabout at the West Auckland bypass onto the A688, go straight on at the next roundabout and the ground is then on the left after around 500 yards.

FC HALIFAX TOWN

Founded: 1911 (Re-formed 2008)
Former Names: Halifax Town FC
Nickname: 'The Shaymen'
Ground: The Shay Stadium, Shay Syke, Halifax, HX1 2YT
Ground Capacity: 10,568
Seating Capacity: 5,285

Record Attendance: 4,023 (1st January 2011)
Pitch Size: 112 × 73 yards
Colours: Blue shirts and shorts
Telephone Nº: (01422) 341222
Fax Number: (01422) 349487
Web Site: www.fcht.co.uk

GENERAL INFORMATION

Car Parking: Adjacent to the East Stand and also Shaw Hill Car Park (Nearby)
Coach Parking: By arrangement with the Club Secretary
Nearest Railway Station: Halifax (10 minutes walk)
Nearest Bus Station: Halifax (15 minutes walk)
Club Shop: At the ground in the East Stand
Opening Times: Please phone for details
Telephone Nº: (01422) 341222 (to change during the 2011/12 season)

GROUND INFORMATION

Away Supporters' Entrances & Sections:
Skircoat Stand (Seating only)

ADMISSION INFO (2016/2017 PRICES)

Adult Standing/Seating: £15.00 – £16.00
Under-16s Standing/Seating: £5.00
Senior Citizen Standing/Seating: £11.00
Under-12s Standing/Seating: £5.00
Under-7s Standing/Seating: £2.00

DISABLED INFORMATION

Wheelchairs: 33 spaces available in total in disabled sections in the East Stand and South Stand
Helpers: One admitted free with each paying disabled fan
Prices: Free of charge for the disabled and helpers
Disabled Toilets: Available in the East and South Stands
Contact: (01422) 434212 (Bookings are not necessary)

Travelling Supporters' Information:
Routes: From the North: Take the A629 to Halifax Town Centre. Take the 2nd exit at the roundabout into Broad Street and follow signs for Huddersfield (A629) into Skircoat Road; From the South, East and West: Exit the M62 at Junction 24 and follow Halifax (A629) signs for the Town Centre into Skircoat Road then Shaw Hill for ground.

FC UNITED OF MANCHESTER

Photo courtesy of John Mills @ Altius Photography

Founded: 2005
Nickname: 'F.C.'
Ground: Broadhurst Park, 310 Lightbowne Road, Moston, Manchester   M40 0FJ
Ground Capacity: 4,400
Seating Capacity: 750
Pitch Size: 110 × 71 yards

Record Attendance: 4,232 (29th May 2015)
Colours: Red shirts with White shorts
Telephone Nº: (0161) 769-2005
Fax Number: (0161) 769-2014
E-mail: office@fc-utd.co.uk
Web Site: www.fc-utd.co.uk

GENERAL INFORMATION

Car Parking: None available at the ground. A number of car parks are located within ½ mile of Broadhurst Park. Please check the club's web site for further information.
Coach Parking: Phone the club on (0161) 769-2005
Nearest Railway Station: Moston (¾ mile)
Nearest Bus Station: A number of services travel to the ground. Please check the club's web site for further details.
Club Shop: At the ground
Opening Times: Matchdays only
Telephone Nº: (0161) 769-2005

GROUND INFORMATION

Away Supporters' Entrances & Sections:
No usual segregation but away fans will be accommodated in the Lightbowne Road End if necessary.

ADMISSION INFO (2016/2017 PRICES)

Adult Seating: £9.00
Senior Citizen (Over-60s)/Student Seating: £5.00
Under-18s Seating: £2.00
Programme Price: £2.00

DISABLED INFORMATION

Wheelchairs: Spaces for wheelchairs are available in all areas of the ground
Helpers: One helper admitted per wheelchair
Prices: Normal prices for wheelchair users. Helpers are admitted free of charge.
Disabled Toilets: Available behind the Main Stand
Contact: (0161) 769-2005   (Bookings are not necessary)

Travelling Supporters' Information: From the M60 travelling clockwise: Exit the M60 at junction 20 and turn onto the A664. At the traffic signals turn left onto the A6104. Travel straight on and then at the Greengate roundabout take the 4th exit onto Lightbowne Road, the B6393. Carry straight on for around a half a mile and Broadhurst Park is on your left; From the M60 travelling anti-clockwise: Exit the M60 at junction 22, then straight on to Hollingwood Avenue, the A6104 . Travel straight on and then at the Greengate roundabout take the 1st exit onto Lightbowne Road, the B6393. Carry straight on for around a half a mile and Broadhurst Park is on your left.

GAINSBOROUGH TRINITY FC

Founded: 1873
Former Names: None
Nickname: 'The Blues'
Ground: Northolme, Gainsborough, Lincolnshire, DN21 2QW
Record Attendance: 9,760 (1948)
Pitch Size: 111 × 71 yards

Colours: Blue shirts and shorts
Telephone Nº: (01427) 611612
Clubhouse Phone Nº: (01427) 613688
Fax Number: (01427) 613295
Ground Capacity: 4,340
Seating Capacity: 504
Web site: www.gainsboroughtrinity.com

GENERAL INFORMATION

Car Parking: Opposite the ground (£2.00 charge).
Coach Parking: Available by prior arrangement
Nearest Railway Station: Lea Road (2 miles) and also Gainsborough Central on Saturdays only (½ mile)
Nearest Bus Station: Heaton Street (1 mile)
Club Shop: At the ground
Opening Times: Matchdays only
Telephone Nº: (01427) 611612

GROUND INFORMATION

Away Supporters' Entrances & Sections:
No usual segregation

ADMISSION INFO (2016/2017 PRICES)

Adult Standing: £12.00
Adult Seating: £12.00
Concessionary Standing: £8.00
Concessionary Seating: £8.00
Under-16s Standing/Seating: £4.00
Under-5s Standing/Seating: Free of charge

DISABLED INFORMATION

Wheelchairs: Accommodated
Helpers: Please phone the club for information
Prices: Normal prices for the disabled. Free for helpers
Disabled Toilets: Available adjacent to the Main Stand
Contact: (01427) 613295 (Bookings are not necessary)

Travelling Supporters' Information:
Routes: From the North, South and West: Exit the A1 at Blyth services taking the 1st left through to Bawtry. In Bawtry, turn right at the traffic lights onto the A631 straight through to Gainsborough (approx. 11 miles). Go over the bridge to the second set of traffic lights and turn left onto the A159 (Scunthorpe Road). Follow the main road past Tesco on the right through the traffic lights. The ground is situated on right approximately a third of a mile north of the Town Centre; From the East: Take the A631 into Gainsborough and turn right onto the A159. Then as above.

GLOUCESTER CITY FC

Gloucester City are groundsharing with Cheltenham Town FC for the 2016/2017 season.

Founded: 1889 **(Re-formed**: 1980)
Forner Names: Gloucester YMCA
Nickname: 'The Tigers'
Ground: Abbey Business Stadium, Whaddon Road, Cheltenham, Gloucestershire GL52 5NA
Ground Capacity: 7,136
Seating Capacity: 4,054

Record Attendance: 8,326 (1956)
Pitch Size: 110 × 72 yards
Colours: Yellow and Black Striped shirts, Black shorts
Telephone Nº: 07813 931781
Web Site: www.gloucestercityafc.com
E-mail: contact@gloucestercityafc.com

GENERAL INFORMATION
Car Parking: Available at the ground.
Coach Parking: At the ground
Nearest Railway Station: Cheltenham Spa (2½ miles)
Nearest Bus Station: Cheltenham Royal Well
Club Shop: At the ground
Opening Times: Matchdays only

GROUND INFORMATION
Away Supporters' Entrances & Sections:
No usual segregation

ADMISSION INFO (2016/2017 PRICES)
Adult Standing: £12.00
Adult Seating: £12.00
Under-18s Standing: Free of charge
Under-18s Seating: Free of charge
Concessionary Standing: £6.00
Concessionary Seating: £6.00

DISABLED INFORMATION
Wheelchairs: Accommodated in front of the Stagecoach West Stand (use main entrance) and in the In 2 Print Stand
Helpers: Admitted free of charge
Prices: Normal prices apply for disabled fans
Disabled Toilets: Available in the In 2 Print Stand, adjacent to the Stagecoach West Stand and in the Social Club
Contact: 07813 931781

Travelling Supporters' Information:
Routes: The ground is situated to the North-East of Cheltenham, 1 mile from the Town Centre off the B4632 (Prestbury Road) – Whaddon Road is to the East of the B4632 just North of Pittville Circus. Road signs in the vicinity indicate 'Whaddon Road/ Cheltenham Town FC'.

HARROGATE TOWN FC

Founded: 1919
Former Names: Harrogate FC and Harrogate Hotspurs FC
Nickname: 'Town'
Ground: CNG Stadium, Wetherby Road, Harrogate, HG2 7SA
Record Attendance: 4,280 (1950)
Pitch Size: 107 × 72 yards

Colours: Yellow and Black striped shirts, Black shorts
Telephone Nº: (01423) 880675
Club Fax Number: (01423) 883671
Ground Capacity: 3,290
Seating Capacity: 502
Web site: www.harrogatetown.com
E-mail: enquiries@harrogatetown.com

GENERAL INFORMATION

Car Parking: Hospital Car Park adjacent
Coach Parking: At the ground
Nearest Railway Station: Harrogate (¾ mile)
Nearest Bus Station: Harrogate
Club Shop: At the ground
Opening Times: Monday to Friday 9.00am to 3.00pm and also on Matchdays
Telephone Nº: (01423) 885525

GROUND INFORMATION

Away Supporters' Entrances & Sections:
No usual segregation

ADMISSION INFO (2016/2017 PRICES)

Adult Standing: £13.00   **Adult Seating**: £14.00
Concessionary Standing: £8.00
Concessionary Seating: £9.00
Student Standing/Seating: £3.00
Under-18s Standing: £3.00
Under-18s Seating: £4.00

DISABLED INFORMATION

Wheelchairs: Accommodated at the front of the Main Stand
Helpers: One helper admitted for each disabled fan
Prices: Free of charge for each disabled fan and helper
Disabled Toilets: Available
Contact: (01423) 880675 (Bookings are necessary)

Travelling Supporters' Information:
Routes: From the South: Take the A61 from Leeds and turn right at the roundabout onto the ring road (signposted York). After about 1¼ miles turn left at the next roundabout onto A661 Wetherby Road. The ground is situated ¾ mile on the right; From the West: Take the A59 straight into Wetherby Road from Empress Roundabout and the ground is on the left; From the East & North: Exit the A1(M) at Junction 47, take the A59 to Harrogate then follow the Southern bypass to Wetherby Road for the A661 Roundabout. Turn right towards Harrogate Town Centre and the ground is on the right after ¾ mile.

KIDDERMINSTER HARRIERS FC

Founded: 1886
Nickname: 'Harriers'
Ground: Aggborough, Hoo Road, Kidderminster, Worcestershire DY10 1NB
Ground Capacity: 6,444
Seating Capacity: 3,143
Record Attendance: 9,155 (1948)

Pitch Size: 110 × 72 yards
Colours: Red and White halved shirts, White shorts
Telephone Nº: (01562) 823931
Fax Number: (01562) 827329
Web Site: www.harriers.co.uk
E-mail: info@harriers.co.uk

GENERAL INFORMATION

Car Parking: At the ground
Coach Parking: As directed
Nearest Railway Station: Kidderminster
Nearest Bus Station: Kidderminster Town Centre
Club Shop: At the ground
Opening Times: Weekdays and First Team Matchdays 9.00am to 5.00pm
Telephone Nº: (01562) 823931

GROUND INFORMATION

Away Supporters' Entrances & Sections:
John Smiths Stand Entrance D and South Terrace Entrance E

ADMISSION INFO (2016/2017 PRICES)

Adult Standing: £13.00
Adult Seating: £15.00
Senior Citizen Standing: £7.00
Senior Citizen Seating: £10.00
Under-16s Standing: £1.00
Under-16s Seating: £1.00

DISABLED INFORMATION

Wheelchairs: Home fans accommodated at the front of the Main Stand, Away fans in front of the John Smiths Stand
Helpers: Admitted
Prices: £10.00 for each disabled fan plus one helper
Disabled Toilets: Available by the disabled area
Contact: (01562) 823931   (Bookings are not necessary)

Travelling Supporters' Information:
Routes: Exit the M5 at Junction 3 and follow the A456 to Kidderminster. The ground is situated close by the Severn Valley Railway Station so follow the brown Steam Train signs and turn into Hoo Road about 200 yards downhill of the station. Follow the road along for ¼ mile and the ground is on the left.

NUNEATON TOWN FC

Founded: 1937 (Reformed 2008)
Former Names: Nuneaton Borough FC
Nickname: 'Boro'
Ground: Liberty Way, Attleborough Fields Industrial Estate, Nuneaton   CV11 6RR
Record Attendance: 3,111 (2nd May 2009)
Pitch Size: 109 × 74 yards

Colours: Blue shirts and white shorts
Telephone Nº: (024) 7638-5738
Fax Number: (024) 7637-2995
Ground Capacity: 4,500
Seating Capacity: 500
Web site: www.nuneatontownfc.com
E-mail: admin@nuneatontownfc.com

GENERAL INFORMATION

Car Parking: On-site car park plus various other parking spaces available on the nearby Industrial Estate (£2.00 fee)
Coach Parking: At the ground (£10.00 fee)
Nearest Railway Station: Nuneaton (2 miles)
Nearest Bus Station: Nuneaton (2 miles)
Club Shop: Yes – The Boro Shop
Opening Times: By appointment and also on matchdays
Telephone Nº: (024) 7638-5738

GROUND INFORMATION

Away Supporters' Entrances & Sections:
No usual segregation

ADMISSION INFO (2016/2017 PRICES)

Adult Standing: £14.00
Adult Seating: £14.00
Concessionary Standing: £12.00
Concessionary Seating: £12.00
Ages 11 to 17 Standing/Seating: £3.00
Under-11s Standing Seating: Free with a paying adult

DISABLED INFORMATION

Wheelchairs: Accommodated, but only 5 spaces are available
Helpers: Admitted
Prices: Normal prices apply for the disabled and helpers
Disabled Toilets: Available
Contact: (024) 7638-5738 (Bookings are necessary)

Travelling Supporters' Information:
Routes: From the South, West and North-West: Exit the M6 at Junction 3 and follow the A444 into Nuneaton. At the Coton Arches roundabout turn right into Avenue Road which is the A4254 signposted for Hinckley. Continue along the A4254 following the road into Garrett Street then Eastboro Way then turn left into Townsend Drive. Follow the road round before turning left into Liberty Way for the ground; From the North: Exit the M1 at Junction 21 and follow the M69. Exit the M69 at Junction 1 and take the 4th exit at the roundabout onto the A5 (Tamworth, Nuneaton). At Longshoot Junction, turn left onto the A47, continue to the roundabout and take the 1st exit onto A4254 Eastborough Way. Turn right at the next roundabout into Townsend Drive then immediately right again for Liberty Way.

SALFORD CITY FC

Founded: 1940
Former Names: Salford FC, Salford Amateurs FC plus a number of other early names
Nickname: 'The Ammies'
Ground: Moor Lane, Kersal, Salford, Manchester, M7 3PZ
Record Attendance: 3,000 (1980)

Colours: Red shirts with White shorts
Telephone N°: (0161) 792-6287
Ground Capacity: 2,163
Seating Capacity: 351 (to increase to 500 during the season)
Pitch Size: 110 × 70 yards
Web site: www.pitchero.com/clubs/salfordcityfc

GENERAL INFORMATION
Car Parking: Street parking only
Coach Parking: At the ground
Nearest Railway Station: Clifton (2½ miles)
Club Shop: At the ground
Opening Times: Matchdays only
Telephone N°: ()161) 792-6287

GROUND INFORMATION
Away Supporters' Entrances & Sections:
No usual segregation

ADMISSION INFO (2016/2017 PRICES)
Adult Standing: £7.00
Adult Seating: £7.00
Senior Citizen/Junior Standing: £3.00
Senior Citizen/Junior Seating: £3.00

DISABLED INFORMATION
Wheelchairs: Accommodated
Helpers: Admitted
Prices: Concessionary prices are charged for the disabled and helpers
Disabled Toilets: Available in the club house
Contact: (0161) 792-6287 (Bookings are not necessary)

Travelling Supporters' Information:
Routes: Exit the M60 at Junction 17 and take the A56 Bury New Road towards Prestwich. Continue along, passing the A6044 (Hilton Lane) road then turn right along Moor Lane heading towards Kersal Moor and the Golf Course. The ground is on the left hand side of the road after a few hundred yards.

STALYBRIDGE CELTIC FC

Founded: 1909
Former Names: None
Nickname: 'Celtic'
Ground: Bower Fold, Mottram Road, Stalybridge, Cheshire   SK15 2RT
Record Attendance: 9,753 (1922/23)
Pitch Size: 109 × 70 yards

Colours: Blue shirts, White shorts and Blue socks
Telephone N°: (0161) 338-2828
Fax Number: (0161) 338-8256
Ground Capacity: 6,108
Seating Capacity: 1,155
Web site: www.stalybridgeceltic.co.uk
E-mail: office@stalybridgeceltic.co.uk

GENERAL INFORMATION

Car Parking: At the ground (£1.00 charge)
Coach Parking: At the ground
Nearest Railway Station: Stalybridge (1 mile)
Nearest Bus Station: Stalybridge town centre
Club Shop: At the ground and also at "Stitch in Time", Market Street, Stalybridge
Opening Times: Matchdays only at the ground Monday to Friday 9.00am to 5.00pm at Market Street
Telephone N°: (0161) 338-2828

GROUND INFORMATION

Away Supporters' Entrances & Sections:
Lockwood & Greenwood Stand on the few occasions when segregation is required. No usual segregation

ADMISSION INFO (2016/2017 PRICES)

Adult Standing: £12.00
Adult Seating: £12.00
Concessionary Standing: £7.00
Concessionary Seating: £7.00
Note: Under-14s are admitted for £2.00 when accompanied by a paying adult

DISABLED INFORMATION

Wheelchairs: 20 spaces available each for home and away fans at the side of the Stepan Stand. A further 9 spaces available in the new Lord Tom Pendry Stand
Helpers: Please phone the club for information
Prices: Please phone the club for information
Disabled Toilets: Available at the rear of the Stepan Stand and at the side of the Lord Tom Pendry Stand
Contact: (0161) 338-2828   (Bookings are necessary)

Travelling Supporters' Information:
Routes: From the Midlands and South: Take the M6, M56, M60 and M67, leaving at the end of the motorway. Go across the roundabout to the traffic lights and turn left. The ground is approximately 2 miles on the left before the Hare & Hounds pub; From the North: Exit the M62 at Junction 18 onto the M60 singposted for Ashton-under-Lyne. Follow the M60 to Junction 24 and join the M67, then as from the Midlands and South.

STOCKPORT COUNTY FC

Photohraph courtesy of Mike Petch – Mphotographic.co.uk

Founded: 1883
Former Names: Heaton Norris Rovers FC
Nickname: 'Hatters' 'County'
Ground: Edgeley Park, Hardcastle Road, Edgeley, Stockport SK3 9DD
Ground Capacity: 10,641 (All seats)
Record Attendance: 27,833 (11th February 1950)
Pitch Size: 111 × 72 yards

Colours: Blue shirts and shorts
Telephone Nº: (0161) 266-2700
Ticket Office: (0161) 266-2700
Web Site: www.stockportcounty.com
E-mail: info@stockportcounty.com

GENERAL INFORMATION

Car Parking: Booth Street (nearby) £4.00
Coach Parking: Booth Street (£20.00)
Nearest Railway Station: Stockport (5 minutes walk)
Nearest Bus Station: Mersey Square (10 minutes walk)
Club Shop: At the ground
Opening Times: Monday to Friday from 12.00pm–4.00pm. Open until 7.45pm on matchdays during the week and also on Saturday matchdays 10.00am – 3.00pm then for 30 minutes after the game.
Telephone Nº: (0161) 266-2700

GROUND INFORMATION

Away Supporters' Entrances & Sections:
Railway End turnstiles for Railway End or turnstiles for Popular Side depending on the opponents

ADMISSION INFO (2016/2017 PRICES)

Adult Seating: £15.00
Under-22s Seating: £10.00
Under-18s Seating: £5.00
Senior Citizen Seating: £10.00
Note: Children under the age of 6 are admitted free.

DISABLED INFORMATION

Wheelchairs: 16 spaces in total. 10 in the Hardcastle Road Stand, 6 in the Cheadle Stand
Helpers: One helper admitted per disabled fan
Prices: £10.00 for the disabled. Helpers free of charge
Disabled Toilets: Yes
Contact: (0161) 266-2700   (Bookings are necessary)

Travelling Supporters' Information:
Routes: From the North, South and West: Exit the M60 at Junction 1 and join the A560, following signs for Cheadle. After ¼ mile turn right into Edgeley Road and after 1 mile turn right into Caroline Street for the ground; From the East: Take the A6 or A560 into Stockport Town Centre and turn left into Greek Street. Take the 2nd exit into Mercian Way (from the roundabout) then turn left into Caroline Street – the ground is straight ahead.

TAMWORTH FC

Founded: 1933
Former Names: None
Nickname: 'The Lambs'
Ground: The Lamb Ground, Kettlebrook, Tamworth, B77 1AA
Record Attendance: 4,920 (3rd April 1948)
Pitch Size: 110 × 73 yards

Colours: Red shirts with Black shorts
Telephone Nº: (01827) 65798
Fax Number: (01827) 62236
Ground Capacity: 4,118
Seating Capacity: 520
Web site: www.thelambs.co.uk

GENERAL INFORMATION

Car Parking: 200 spaces available at the ground – £2.00 per car, £5.00 for per minibus or £10.00 per coach
Coach Parking: At the ground
Nearest Railway Station: Tamworth (½ mile)
Nearest Bus Station: Tamworth (½ mile)
Club Shop: At the ground
Opening Times: Weekdays from 10.00am to 4.00pm and also on Matchdays
Telephone Nº: (01827) 65798 Option 3

GROUND INFORMATION

Away Supporters' Entrances & Sections:
Gates 1 and 2 for Terracing, Gate 2A for seating

ADMISSION INFO (2016/2017 PRICES)

Adult Standing: £12.00
Adult Seating: £14.00
Under-18s Standing: £4.00
Under-18s Seating: £6.00
Under-16s Standing: £2.00 (Under-5s free)
Under-16s Seating: £4.00
Under-5s Seating: £2.00
Senior Citizen Standing: £7.00
Senior Citizen Seating: £9.00

DISABLED INFORMATION

Wheelchairs: Accommodated
Helpers: Admitted
Prices: Normal prices apply for Wheelchair disabled. Helpers are charged concessionary rates
Disabled Toilets: Yes
Contact: (01827) 65798 (Bookings are advisable)

Travelling Supporters' Information:
Routes: Exit the M42 at Junction 10 and take the A5/A51 to the town centre following signs for Town Centre/Snowdome. The follow signs for Kettlebrook and the ground is in Kettlebrook Road, 50 yards from the traffic island by the Railway Viaduct and the Snowdome. The ground is signposted from all major roads.

WORCESTER CITY FC

Worcester City FC are groundsharing with Bromsgrove Sporting FC during the 2016/2017 season.

Founded: 1902
Former Names: Berwick Rangers FC
Nickname: 'The City'
Ground: Victoria Ground, Birmingham Road, Bromsgrove   B61 0DR
Record Attendance: 7,563 (1957/58 season)
Ground Capacity: 3,500   **Seating Capacity**: 375
Record Attendance: 17,042 (1959 vs Sheffield Utd)

Pitch Size: 110 × 72 yards
Colours: Blue and White striped shirts, Blue shorts
Office Address: Unit 7, Ball Mill Top Business Park, Hallow, Worcester   WR2 6LS
Telephone Nº: (01905) 23003
Web site: www.worcestercityfc.com
E-mail: office@worcestercityfc.com

GENERAL INFORMATION

Car Parking: 200 spaces available at the ground
Coach Parking: By Police Direction
Nearest Railway Station: Bromsgrove (1½ miles)
Nearest Bus Station: 500 yards
Club Shop: Online sales only at present
Telephone Nº: (01905) 23003

GROUND INFORMATION

Away Supporters' Entrances & Sections:
No usual segregation

ADMISSION INFO (2016/2017 PRICES)

Adult Standing/Seating: £13.00
Under-16s Standing/Seating: £3.00
Young Adult Standing/Seating: £6.00
Senior Citizen Standing/Seating: £9.00

DISABLED INFORMATION

Wheelchairs: Accommodated
Helpers: Admitted
Prices: Normal prices for the disabled. Free for helpers
Disabled Toilets: Available by the disabled area
Contact: (01905) 23003   (Bookings are necessary)

Travelling Supporters' Information:
Routes: From the North: Exit the M42 at Junction 1 and follow the A38 towards Bromsgrove. Once in Bromsgrove, follow the Town Centre signs at the traffic lights. Victoria Ground is approximately 2 minutes away next to Clark's Motor Services on the right hand side; From the South: Exit the M5 at Junction 4 onto the A38. Then as above.

THE VANARAMA NATIONAL LEAGUE SOUTH

Address

4th Floor, 20 Waterloo Street,
Birmingham B2 5TB

Phone (0121) 643-3143

Web site www.footballconference.co.uk

Clubs for the 2016/2017 Season

Bath City FC .... Page 54
Bishop's Stortford FC .... Page 55
Chelmsford City FC .... Page 56
Concord Rangers FC .... Page 57
Dartford FC .... Page 58
Eastbourne Borough FC .... Page 59
East Thurrock United FC .... Page 60
Ebbsfleet United FC .... Page 61
Gosport Borough FC .... Page 62
Hampton & Richmond Borough FC .... Page 63
Hemel Hempstead Town FC .... Page 64
Hungerford Town FC .... Page 65
Maidenhead United FC .... Page 66
Margate FC .... Page 67
Oxford City FC .... Page 68
Poole Town FC .... Page 69
St. Albans City FC .... Page 70
Truro City FC .... Page 71
Wealdstone FC .... Page 72
Welling United FC .... Page 73
Weston-super-Mare FC .... Page 74
Whitehawk FC .... Page 75

BATH CITY FC

Founded: 1889
Former Names: Bath AFC, Bath Railway FC and Bath Amateurs FC
Nickname: 'The Romans'
Ground: Twerton Park, Bath BA2 1DB
Record Attendance: 18,020 (1960)
Pitch Size: 110 × 76 yards

Colours: Black and White striped shirts, Black shorts
Telephone Nº: (01225) 423087
Ground Capacity: 8,840
Seating Capacity: 1,026
Web site: www.bathcityfc.com
E-mail: info@bathcityfootballclub.co.uk

GENERAL INFORMATION

Car Parking: 150 spaces available at the ground
Coach Parking: Available at the ground
Nearest Railway Station: Oldfield Park (1 mile)
Nearest Bus Station: Dorchester Street, Bath
Club Shop: Yes – c/o Club
Opening Times: Matchdays and office hours
Telephone Nº: (01225) 423087

GROUND INFORMATION

Away Supporters' Entrances & Sections:
Turnstiles 17-19

ADMISSION INFO (2016/2017 PRICES)

Adult Standing/Seating: £13.00
Senior Citizen Standing/Seating: £10.00
Students/Under-18s Standing/Seating: £7.00
Under-16s Standing/Seating: £2.00

DISABLED INFORMATION

Wheelchairs: 10 spaces available each for home and away fans in front of the Family Stand
Helpers: Admitted
Prices: Normal prices for the disabled. Free for helpers
Disabled Toilets: Available behind the Family Stand
Contact: (01225) 423087   (Bookings are necessary)

Travelling Supporters' Information:
Route: As a recommendation, avoid exiting the M4 at Junction 18 as the road takes you through Bath City Centre. Instead, exit the M4 at Junction 19 onto the M32. Turn off the M32 at Junction 1 and follow the A4174 Bristol Ring Road south then join the A4 for Bath. On the A4, after passing through Saltford you will reach a roundabout shortly before entering Bath. Take the 2nd exit at this roundabout then follow the road before turning left into Newton Road at the bottom of the steep hill. The ground is then on the right hand side of the road.

BISHOP'S STORTFORD FC

Founded: 1874
Former Names: None
Nickname: 'Blues' 'Bishops'
Ground: The Prokit Stadium, Woodside Park, Dunmow Road, Bishop's Stortford   CM23 5RG
Record Attendance: 3,555 (2000)
Pitch Size: 110 × 70 yards

Colours: Blue and White shirts with Blue shorts
Telephone N°: (01279) 306456
Fax Number: (01279) 715621
Ground Capacity: 4,000
Seating Capacity: 225
Web site: www.bsfc.co.uk

GENERAL INFORMATION
Car Parking: 500 spaces available at the ground
Coach Parking: At the ground
Nearest Railway Station: Bishop's Stortford
Nearest Bus Station: Bishop's Stortford
Club Shop: At the ground
Opening Times: Matchdays only 1.30pm to 5.00pm
Telephone N°: (01279) 306456

GROUND INFORMATION
Away Supporters' Entrances & Sections:
No usual segregation

ADMISSION INFO (2016/2017 PRICES)
Adult Standing/Seating: £13.00
Concessionary Standing/Seating: £8.00
Student Standing/Seating: £7.00
Under-16s Standing/Seating: £6.00
Note: Under-12s are admitted free of charge when accompanied by a paying adult.

DISABLED INFORMATION
Wheelchairs: Accommodated in the disabled section
Helpers: Admitted
Prices: Free of charge for the disabled and helpers
Disabled Toilets: Yes
Contact: (01279) 306456   (Bookings are not necessary)

Travelling Supporters' Information:
Routes: Exit the M11 at junction 8 and take the A1250 towards Bishop Stortford. Turn left at the first roundabout and the ground is first right opposite the Golf Club (the entrance is between Industrial Units).

CHELMSFORD CITY FC

Founded: 1938
Former Names: Chelmsford FC
Nickname: 'City' or 'Clarets'
Ground: Melbourne Community Stadium, Salerno Way, Chelmsford   CM1 2EH
Record Attendance: 16,807 (at previous ground)
Pitch Size: 109 × 70 yards

Colours: Claret and White shirts and shorts
Telephone Nº: (01245) 290959
Ground Capacity: 3,000
Seating Capacity: 1,400
Web site: www.chelmsfordcityfc.com

GENERAL INFORMATION

Car Parking: Limited space at ground and street parking
Coach Parking: Two spaces available at the ground subject to advance notice
Nearest Railway Station: Chelmsford (2 miles)
Nearest Bus Station: Chelmsford (2 miles)
Club Shop: At the ground
Opening Times: Matchdays only at present
Telephone Nº: (01245) 290959

GROUND INFORMATION

Away Supporters' Entrances & Sections:
No usual segregation

ADMISSION INFO (2016/2017 PRICES)

Adult Standing: £13.00
Adult Seating: £13.00
Under-18s Standing: £5.00
Under-18s Seating: £5.00
Under-12s Standing: Free of charge
Under-12s Seating: Free of charge
Concessionary Standing: £9.00
Concessionary Seating: £9.00

DISABLED INFORMATION

Wheelchairs: Spaces for 11 wheelchairs available
Helpers: Admitted free of charge
Prices: Disabled fans are charged standing admission prices
Disabled Toilets: Available
Contact: (01245) 290959   (Bookings are necessary)

Travelling Supporters' Information:
Route: The ground is situated next to the only set of high rise flats in Chelmsford which can therefore be used as a landmark. From the A12 from London: Exit the A12 at Junction 15 signposted for Chelmsford/Harlow/A414 and head towards Chelmsford along the dual-carriageway. At the third roundabout, immediately after passing the 'Superbowl' on the left, take the first exit into Westway, signposted for the Crematorium and Widford Industrial Estate. Continue along Westway which becomes Waterhouse Lane after the second set of traffic lights. At the next set of lights (at the gyratory system) take the first exit into Rainsford Road, signposted for Sawbridgeworth A1060. Continue along Rainsford Road then turn right into Chignal Road at the second set of traffic lights. Turn right again into Melbourne Avenue and Salerno Way is on the left at the end of the football pitches.

CONCORD RANGERS FC

Founded: 1967
Former Names: None
Nickname: 'The Beachboys'
Ground: Aspect Arena, Thames Road, Canvey Island, SS8 0HH
Record Attendance: 1,800

Colours: Yellow shirts with Yellow shorts
Telephone Nº: (01268) 515750
Ground Capacity: 3,000
Seating Capacity: 340
Web Site: www.concordrangers.co.uk

GENERAL INFORMATION
Car Parking: At the ground
Coach Parking: At the ground
Nearest Railway Station: Benfleet
Club Shop: Available via the club's web site shortly
Opening Times: –
Telephone Nº: –

GROUND INFORMATION
Away Supporters' Entrances & Sections:
No usual segregation

ADMISSION INFO (2016/2017 PRICES)
Adult Standing: £10.00
Adult Seating: £10.00
Senior Citizen Standing: £5.00
Senior Citizen Seating: £5.00
Under-16s Standing/Seating: £3.00
Under-10s Standing/Seating: Free of charge

DISABLED INFORMATION
Wheelchairs: Accommodated
Helpers: Admitted
Prices: Normal prices apply for the disabled and helpers
Disabled Toilets: Available
Contact: (01268) 515750   (Bookings are necessary)

Travelling Supporters' Information:
Routes: Take the A13 to the A130 (Canvey Way) for Canvey Island. At the Benfleet roundabout, take the 3rd exit into Canvey Road and continue along through Charfleets Service Road into Long Road. Take the 5th turn on the right into Thorney Bay Road and Thames Road is the 3rd turn on the right. The ground is on the left-hand side around 300 yards down Thames Road.

DARTFORD FC |

Founded: 1888
Former Names: None
Nickname: 'The Darts'
Ground: Princes Park Stadium, Grassbanks, Darenth Road, Dartford   DA1 1RT
Record Attendance: 4,097 (11th November 2006)
Pitch Size: 110 × 71 yards

Colours: White Shirts with Black Shorts
Telephone Nº: (01322) 299990
Fax Number: (01322) 299996
Ground Capacity: 4,118
Seating Capacity: 640
Web Site: www.dartfordfc.com
E-mail: info@dartfordfc.com

GENERAL INFORMATION
Car Parking: At the ground
Coach Parking: At the ground
Nearest Railway Station: Dartford (½ mile)
Nearest Bus Station: Dartford (½ mile) & Bluewater (2 miles)
Club Shop: At the ground
Opening Times: Matchdays only – 1.00pm to 6.00pm (but the stadium itself is open daily).
Telephone Nº: (01322) 299990

ADMISSION INFO (2016/2017 PRICES)
Adult Standing: £14.00
Adult Seating: £14.00
Senior Citizen/Concessionary Standing: £7.00
Senior Citizen/Concessionary Seating: £7.00
Youth (Ages 13 to 17) Standing/Seating: £5.00
Junior (Ages 5 to 12) Standing/Seating: £2.00
Under-5s Standing/Seating: Free of charge

DISABLED INFORMATION
Wheelchairs: Accommodated
Helpers: Admitted
Prices: Concessionary prices for the disabled and helpers
Disabled Toilets: Available
Contact: (01322) 299991   (Bookings are not necessary)

Travelling Supporters' Information:
Routes: From M25 Clockwise: Exit the M25 at Junction 1B. At the roundabout, take the 3rd exit onto Princes Road (A225) then the second exit at the next roundabout. * Continue downhill to the traffic lights (with the ground on the left), turn left into Darenth Road then take the 2nd left for the Car Park; From M25 Anti-clockwise: Exit the M25 at Junction 2 and follow the A225 to the roundabout. Take the first exit at this roundabout then the 2nd exit at the next roundabout. Then as from * above.

EASTBOURNE BOROUGH FC

Founded: 1963
Former Names: Langney Sports FC
Nickname: 'The Sports'
Ground: Langney Sports Club, Priory Lane, Langney, Eastbourne BN23 7QH
Record Attendance: 3,770 (5th November 2005)
Pitch Size: 115 × 72 yards

Colours: Red shirts with Black shorts
Telephone Nº: (01323) 766265
Fax Number: (01323) 741627
Ground Capacity: 4,151
Seating Capacity: 542
Web site: www.ebfc.co.uk

GENERAL INFORMATION

Car Parking: Around 400 spaces available at the ground
Coach Parking: At the ground
Nearest Railway Station: Pevensey & Westham (1½ miles but no public transport to the ground)
Nearest Bus Station: Eastbourne (Service 6A to ground)
Club Shop: At the ground
Opening Times: Matchdays only
Telephone Nº: (01323) 766265

GROUND INFORMATION

Away Supporters' Entrances & Sections:
No usual segregation

ADMISSION INFO (2016/2017 PRICES)

Adult Standing: £12.00
Adult Seating: £12.00
Under-16s Standing: £1.00
Under-16s Seating: £1.00
Senior Citizen Standing: £8.00
Senior Citizen Seating: £8.00

DISABLED INFORMATION

Wheelchairs: 6 spaces available
Helpers: Admitted
Prices: Normal prices apply
Disabled Toilets: Available
Contact: (01323) 766265 (Bookings are necessary)

Travelling Supporters' Information:
Routes: From the North: Exit the A22 onto the Polegate bypass, signposted A27 Eastbourne, Hastings & Bexhill. *Take the 2nd exit at the next roundabout for Stone Cross and Westham (A22) then the first exit at the following roundabout signposted Stone Cross and Westham. Turn right after ½ mile into Friday Street (B2104). At the end of Friday Street, turn left at the double mini-roundabout into Hide Hollow (B2191), passing Eastbourne Crematorium on your right. Turn right at the roundabout into Priory Road, and Priory Lane is about 200 yards down the road on the left; Approaching on the A27 from Brighton: Turn left at the Polegate traffic lights then take 2nd exit at the large roundabout to join the bypass. Then as from *.

EAST THURROCK UNITED FC

Founded: 1969
Former Names: None
Nickname: 'The Rocks'
Ground: Rookery Hill, Corringham, Essex, SS17 9LB
Record Attendance: 1,250 (vs Woking, 2003)
Pitch Size: 110 × 72 yards

Colours: Amber shirts with Black shorts
Telephone Nº: (01375) 644166
Ground Capacity: 3,500
Seating Capacity: 250
Web: www.pitchero.com/clubs/eastthurrockunited

GENERAL INFORMATION

Car Parking: At the ground
Coach Parking: At the ground
Nearest Railway Station: Stanford-le-Hope (2 miles)
Nearest Bus Station: Stanford-le-Hope (2 miles)
Club Shop: None
Opening Times: –

GROUND INFORMATION

Away Supporters' Entrances & Sections:
No usual segregation

ADMISSION INFO (2016/2017 PRICES)

Adult Standing: £12.00
Adult Seating: £12.00
Senior Citizen Standing: £6.00
Senior Citizen Seating: £6.00
Under-16s Standing: £3.00
Under-16s Seating: £3.00

DISABLED INFORMATION

Wheelchairs: Accommodated
Helpers: Admitted
Prices: Standard prices apply
Disabled Toilets: Available
Contact: 07885 313435 (Bookings are necessary)

Travelling Supporters' Information:
Routes: Exit the M25 at Junction 30 and follow the A13 East. At Stanford-le-Hope turn-off on to the A1014 Coryton, cross over the roundabout and pass through the traffic lights. Then take the first turning on the left signposted Corringham and the ground is immediately on the left.

EBBSFLEET UNITED FC

Founded: 1946
Former Names: Gravesend & Northfleet United FC, Gravesend United FC and Northfleet United FC
Nickname: 'The Fleet'
Ground: Stonebridge Road, Northfleet, Gravesend, Kent DA11 9GN
Record Attendance: 12,063 (1963)
Pitch Size: 112 × 72 yards

Colours: Reds shirts with White shorts
Telephone Nº: (01474) 533796
Fax Number: (01474) 324754
Ground Capacity: 5,258
Seating Capacity: 1,220
Web site: www.ebbsfleetunited.co.uk
E-mail: info@eufc.co.uk

GENERAL INFORMATION

Car Parking: Ebbsfleet International Car Park C (when available) and also street parking
Coach Parking: At the ground
Nearest Railway Station: Northfleet (5 minutes walk)
Nearest Bus Station: Bus Stop outside the ground
Club Shop: At the ground
Opening Times: Matchdays only
Telephone Nº: (01474) 533796

GROUND INFORMATION

Away Supporters' Entrances & Sections:
Only certain games are segregated, when the Swanscombe End turnstiles are allocated to away supporters.
Please contact the club for further details

ADMISSION INFO (2016/2017 PRICES)

Adult Standing: £12.00
Adult Seating: £12.00
Concessionary Standing: £9.00
Concessionary Seating: £9.00
Under-16s Standing/Seating: £5.00
Under-12s Standing/Seating: Free of charge when accompanied by a paying adult.

DISABLED INFORMATION

Wheelchairs: 6 spaces are available in the Disabled Area in front of the Main Stand
Helpers: Admitted free of charge
Prices: Please phone the club for information
Disabled Toilets: Available in the Main Stand
Contact: (01474) 533796 (Bookings are necessary)

Travelling Supporters' Information:
Routes: Take the A2 to the Northfleet/Southfleet exit and follow signs for Northfleet (B262). Go straight on at the first roundabout then take the 2nd exit at the 2nd roundabout into Thames Way and follow the football signs for the ground.

GOSPORT BOROUGH FC

Founded: 1944
Former Names: Gosport Borough Athletic FC
Nickname: 'The Boro'
Ground: The Aerial Direct Stadium, Privett Park, Privett Road, Gosport, PO12 3SX
Record Attendance: 4,770 (1951)

Colours: Yellow shirts with Navy Blue shorts
Telephone Nº: (023) 9250-1042 (Matchdays only)
Fax Number: (01329) 235961
Ground Capacity: 4,500
Seating Capacity: 450
Web Site: www.gosportboroughfc.co.uk

GENERAL INFORMATION
Car Parking: At the ground
Coach Parking: At the ground
Nearest Railway Station: Fareham (5½ miles)
Club Shop: At the ground
Opening Times: Matchdays only
Telephone Nº: –

GROUND INFORMATION
Away Supporters' Entrances & Sections:
No usual segregation

ADMISSION INFO (2016/2017 PRICES)
Adult Standing: £13.00
Adult Seating: £13.00
Concessionary Standing: £9.00
Concessionary Seating: £9.00
Under-18s Standing/Seating: £5.00
Note: Under-12s are admitted free of charge when accompanied by a paying adult

DISABLED INFORMATION
Wheelchairs: Accommodated
Helpers: Admitted
Prices: Normal prices apply for the disabled and helpers
Disabled Toilets: Available
Contact: (023) 9250-1042 (Bookings are not necessary)

Travelling Supporters' Information:
Routes: Exit the M27 at Junction 11 and follow take the A27 Eastern Way towards Gosport. Turn left at the roundabout to join the A32 Gosport Road and head south into Gosport. Continue along the A32 as it becomes Fareham Road then, at the second roundabout in a junction with two roundabouts, take the 3rd exit (signposted Alverstoke, Stokes Bay, Privett Park) into Military Road. Continue straight down this road, pass the playing fields on the left, then turn left at the roundabout into Privett Road. The entrance to the ground is the 4th turning on the left, just after the junction with Privett Place.

HAMPTON & RICHMOND BOROUGH FC

Founded: 1921
Former Names: Hampton FC
Nickname: 'Beavers'
Ground: Beveree Stadium, Beaver Close,
off Station Road, Hampton, Middlesex   TW12 2BT
Record Attendance: 3,500 vs West Ham United
Pitch Size: 113 × 71 yards

Colours: Blue shirts with Red flash, Blue shorts
Matchday Phone Nº: (020) 8979-2456
Fax Number: (020) 8979-2456
Ground Capacity: 3,500
Seating Capacity: 300
Web site: www.hamptonfc.net

GENERAL INFORMATION

Car Parking: At the ground and street parking
Coach Parking: Contact the Club for information
Nearest Railway Station: Hampton
Nearest Bus Station: Hounslow/Kingston/Fulwell
Club Shop: At the ground
Opening Times: Matchdays only
Telephone Nº: None

GROUND INFORMATION

Away Supporters' Entrances & Sections:
No usual segregation

ADMISSION INFO (2016/2017 PRICES)

Adult Standing: £12.00
Adult Seating: £12.00
Senior Citizen/Concessionary Standing: £8.00
Senior Citizen/Concessionary Seating: £8.00
Under-16s Standing/Seating: £3.00
Note: Under-5s are admitted free of charge
Programme Price: £2.50

DISABLED INFORMATION

Wheelchairs: Accommodated
Helpers: Admitted
Prices: Normal prices apply
Disabled Toilets: Available
Contact: (020) 8979-2456   (Bookings are not necessary)

Travelling Supporters' Information:
Routes: From the South: Exit the M3 at Junction 1 and follow the A308 (signposted Kingston). Turn 1st left after Kempton Park into Percy Road. Turn right at the level crossing into Station Road then left into Beaver Close for the ground; From the North: Take the A305 from Twickenham then turn left onto the A311. Pass through Hampton Hill onto Hampton High Street. Turn right at the White Hart pub (just before the junction with the A308), then right into Station Road and right again into Beaver Close.

HEMEL HEMPSTEAD TOWN FC

Founded: 1885
Former Names: Apsley FC and Hemel Hempstead FC
Nickname: 'The Tudors'
Ground: Vauxhall Road, Adeyfield, Hemel Hempstead HP2 4HW
Record Attendance: 2,254 (vs Gosport Borough during the 2013/14 season)

Pitch Size: 112 × 72 yards
Colours: Shirts and Shorts are Red with White trim
Telephone Nº: (01442) 264300
Fax Number: (01442) 264322
Ground Capacity: 3,000
Seating Capacity: 350
Web site: www.hemelfc.com

GENERAL INFORMATION
Car Parking: At the ground
Coach Parking: At the ground
Nearest Railway Station: Hemel Hempstead (1½ miles)
Nearest Bus Station: Hemel Hempstead (¾ mile)
Club Shop: None

GROUND INFORMATION
Away Supporters' Entrances & Sections:
No usual segregation

ADMISSION INFO (2016/2017 PRICES)
Adult Standing: £12.00
Adult Seating: £12.00
Concessionary Standing/Seating: £8.00
Under-18s Standing/Seating: £4.00
Under-12s Standing/Seating: £1.00
Programme Price: £2.00

DISABLED INFORMATION
Wheelchairs: Accommodated
Helpers: Admitted
Prices: Normal prices apply
Disabled Toilets: Available in the Clubhouse
Contact: (01442) 259777

Travelling Supporters' Information:
Routes: Exit the M1 at Junction 8 and go straight ahead at the first roundabout. When approaching the 2nd roundabout move into the right hand lane and, as you continue straight across be ready to turn right almost immediately through a gap in the central reservation. This turn-off is Leverstock Green Road and continue along this to the double mini-roundabout. At this roundabout turn left into Vauxhall Road and the ground is on the right at the next roundabout.

HUNGERFORD TOWN FC

Founded: 1886
Former Names: Hungerford Swifts FC
Nickname: 'The Crusaders'
Ground: Town Ground, Bulpit Lane, Hungerford, RG17 0AY
Record Attendance: 1,684 (1988/89 season)

Colours: White shirts with Black shorts
Contact Telephone Nº: (01488) 682939
Ground Capacity: 2,500
Seating Capacity: 250
Web: www.pitchero.com/clubs/hungerfordtownfc

GENERAL INFORMATION

Car Parking: At the ground and at the local school
Coach Parking: At the ground
Nearest Railway Station: Hungerford (½ mile)
Club Shop: At the ground
Opening Times: Monday to Friday 6.30pm to 11.00pm and Saturday from 12.00pm to midnight
Telephone Nº: (01488) 682939

GROUND INFORMATION

Away Supporters' Entrances & Sections:
No usual segregation

ADMISSION INFO (2016/2017 PRICES)

Adult Standing: £12.00
Adult Seating: £12.00
Senior Citizen/Junior Standing: £6.00
Senior Citizen/Junior Seating: £6.00
Programme Price: £2.00

DISABLED INFORMATION

Wheelchairs: Accommodated
Helpers: Admitted
Prices: £6.00 for the disabled. Free of charge for helpers
Disabled Toilets: Available
Contact: (01488) 682939   (Bookings are not necessary)

Travelling Supporters' Information:
Routes: Exit the M4 at Junction 14 and take the A338 towards Hungerford. Upon reaching Hungerford, turn right at the roundabout onto the A4 Bath Road, turn left at the next rounabout into Charnham Street then turn left again into Bridge Street (A338). The road becomes the High Street and pass under the railway line, carry straight on over three mini-roundabouts then take the next left into Priory Road. Continue to the end of the street and continue left into Priory Road then take the 3rd turning on the left into Bulpit Lane. The entrance to the ground is on the left shortly after crossing the junction with Priory Avenue.

MAIDENHEAD UNITED FC

Founded: 1870
Former Names: None
Nickname: 'Magpies'
Ground: York Road, Maidenhead, Berks. SL6 1SF
Record Attendance: 7,920 (1936)
Pitch Size: 110 × 75 yards

Colours: Black and White striped shirts, Black shorts
Telephone Nº: (01628) 636314 (Club)
Contact Number: (01628) 636078
Ground Capacity: 4,500
Seating Capacity: 400
Web: www.pitchero.com/clubs/maidenheadunited

GENERAL INFORMATION

Car Parking: Street parking
Coach Parking: Street parking
Nearest Railway Station: Maidenhead (¼ mile)
Nearest Bus Station: Maidenhead
Club Shop: At the ground
Opening Times: Matchdays only
Telephone Nº: (01628) 624739

GROUND INFORMATION

Away Supporters' Entrances & Sections:
No usual segregation

ADMISSION INFO (2016/2017 PRICES)

Adult Standing: £10.00
Adult Seating: £10.00
Concessionary Standing and Seating: £6.00
Under-16s Standing and Seating: £3.00
Note: Junior Magpies (Under-16s) are admitted free to matches in the League.

DISABLED INFORMATION

Wheelchairs: Accommodated
Helpers: Admitted
Prices: Normal prices for the disabled. Free for helpers
Disabled Toilets: Available
Contact: (01628) 636078 (Bookings are not necessary)

Travelling Supporters' Information:
Routes: Exit M4 at Junction 7 and take the A4 to Maidenhead. Cross the River Thames bridge and turn left at the 2nd roundabout passing through the traffic lights. York Road is first right and the ground is approximately 300 yards along on the left.

MARGATE FC

Founded: 1896
Former Names: Thanet United FC
Nickname: 'The Gate'
Ground: Hartsdown Park, Hartsdown Road, Margate   CT9 5QZ
Record Attendance: 14,500 vs Spurs (1973)

Colours: Royal Blue shirts and shorts
Telephone Nº: (01843) 221769
Fax Number: (01843) 221769
Ground Capacity: 2,000
Seating Capacity: 350
Web site: www.margate-fc.co.uk

GENERAL INFORMATION

Car Parking: Limited spaces at the ground for £2.00 plus street parking
Coach Parking: Available at the ground
Nearest Railway Station: Margate (10 minutes walk)
Club Shop: At the ground
Opening Times: Monday to Friday 9.00am to 5.00pm
Telephone Nº: (01843) 225566

GROUND INFORMATION

Away Supporters' Entrances & Sections:
Segregation only used for selected fixtures

ADMISSION INFO (2016/2017 PRICES)

Adult Standing: £12.00
Adult Seating: £12.00
Concessionary Standing: £10.00
Concessionary Seating: £10.00
Ages 11 to 17 Standing: £5.00
Ages 11 to 17 Seating: £5.00
Under-11s Standing/Seating: £1.00
Programme Price: £2.00

DISABLED INFORMATION

Wheelchairs: Accommodated
Helpers: Admitted
Prices: Concessionary prices apply
Disabled Toilets: Available
Contact: (01843) 221769   (Bookings are necessary)

Travelling Supporters' Information:
Routes: Take the M2/A2 to the A299 then the A28 (Thanet Way) into Margate, turn right opposite the Dog & Duck Pub into Hartsdown Road. Proceed over the crossroads and the ground is on the left.

OXFORD CITY FC

Founded: 1882
Former Names: None
Nickname: 'City'
Ground: The Oxford City Community Arena, Marsh Lane, Marston, Oxford OX3 0NQ
Record Attendance: 9,500 (1950)

Colours: Blue & White hooped shirts with Blue shorts
Telephone Nº: (01865) 744493 or 07817 885396
Ground Capacity: 3,000
Seating Capacity: 300
Web Site: www.oxfordcityfc.co.uk
E-mail: ctoxford@btinternet.com

GENERAL INFORMATION
Car Parking: At the ground
Coach Parking: At the ground
Nearest Railway Station: Oxford (3¾ miles)
Club Shop: At the ground
Opening Times: Matchdays only
Telephone Nº: (01865) 744493

GROUND INFORMATION
Away Supporters' Entrances & Sections:
No usual segregation

ADMISSION INFO (2016/2017 PRICES)
Adult Standing: £12.00
Adult Seating: £12.00
Concessionary Standing: £6.00
Concessionary Seating: £6.00
Student Standing: £3.00
Student Seating: £3.00
Under-16s Standing: Free of charge
Under-16s Seating: Free of charge

DISABLED INFORMATION
Wheelchairs: Accommodated
Helpers: Admitted
Prices: Normal prices apply for the disabled and helpers
Disabled Toilets: Available
Contact: (01865) 744493 (Bookings are not necessary)

Travelling Supporters' Information:
Routes: The stadium is located by the side of the A40 Northern Bypass Road next to the Marston flyover junction to the north east of Oxford. Exit the A40 at the Marston junction and head into Marsh Lane (B4150). Take the first turn on the left into the OXSRAD Complex then turn immediately left again to follow the approach road to the stadium in the far corner of the site.

POOLE TOWN FC

Founded: 1880
Former Names: Various names including Poole FC and Poole St. Marys FC
Nickname: 'The Dolphins'
Ground: Tatnam Farm, School Lane, Poole, BH15 3JR
Record Attendance: 1,652 (26/3/2011 at Tatnam)
Pitch Size: 110 × 73 yards

Colours: Red & White halved shirts with Red shorts
Telephone Nº: (01794) 640104
Office Address: 153 High Street, Poole BH15 1AU
Ground Capacity: 2,000
Seating Capacity: 152
Web Site: www.pooletownfc.co.uk

GENERAL INFORMATION
Car Parking: At the ground
Coach Parking: At the ground
Nearest Railway Station: Poole (¾ mile)
Nearest Bus Station: Poole
Club Shop: At the ground
Opening Times: Matchdays only
Telephone Nº: (01794) 640104

GROUND INFORMATION
Away Supporters' Entrances & Sections:
No usual segregation

ADMISSION INFO (2016/2017 PRICES)
Adult Standing: £12.00
Adult Seating: £12.00
Senior Citizen Standing: £8.00
Senior Citizen Seating: £8.00
Under-18s Standing/Seating: £5.00
Under-13s Standing/Seating: £1.00

DISABLED INFORMATION
Wheelchairs: Accommodated
Helpers: Admitted
Prices: Normal prices apply for the disabled and helpers
Disabled Toilets: One available
Contact: (01794) 681167 (Bookings are not necessary)

Travelling Supporters' Information:
Routes: Take the A35, A3049 or the A349 into Poole to the Fleetsbridge Interchange where these roads all meet. At the interchange, takes the Fleets Lane exit and head southwards into the centre of Poole. Continue along Fleets Lane into Stanley Green Road (passing the Retail Park and part of the Industrial Estate) for approximately ½ mile then turn left into Palmer Road. Take the first turning on the right into School Lane for the ground.

ST. ALBANS CITY FC

Founded: 1908
Former Names: None
Nickname: 'The Saints'
Ground: Clarence Park, York Road, St. Albans, Hertfordshire   AL1 4PL
Record Attendance: 9,757 (27th February 1926)
Pitch Size: 110 × 80 yards

Colours: Blue shirts with Yellow trim, Blue shorts
Telephone Nº: (01727) 848914
Fax Number: (01727) 848914
Ground Capacity: 5,007
Seating Capacity: 667
Web site: www.stalbanscityfc.com

GENERAL INFORMATION
Car Parking: Street parking
Coach Parking: In Clarence Park
Nearest Railway Station: St. Albans City (200 yds)
Club Shop: At the ground
Opening Times: Matchdays only
Telephone Nº: (01727) 864296

GROUND INFORMATION
Away Supporters' Entrances & Sections:
Hatfield Road End when matches are segregated

ADMISSION INFO (2016/2017 PRICES)
Adult Standing/Seating: £15.00
Concessionary Standing/Seating: £10.00
Under-16s Standing/Seating: £5.00
Note: Under-12s are admitted free of charge when accompanied by a paying adult
Programme Price: £2.50

DISABLED INFORMATION
Wheelchairs: Accommodated
Helpers: One admitted per disabled supporter
Prices: Free for disabled, concessionary prices for helpers
Disabled Toilets: Available in the York Road End
Contact: (01727) 864296   (Bookings are not necessary)

Travelling Supporters' Information:
Routes: Take the M1 or M10 to the A405 North Orbital Road and at the roundabout at the start of the M10, go north on the A5183 (Watling Street). Turn right along St. Stephen's Hill and carry along into St. Albans. Continue up Holywell Hill, go through two sets of traffic lights and at the end of St. Peter's Street, take a right turn at the roundabout into Hatfield Road. Follow over the mini-roundabouts and at the second set of traffic lights turn left into Clarence Road and the ground is on the left. Park in Clarence Road and enter the ground via the Park or in York Road and use the entrance by the footbridge.

TRURO CITY FC

Founded: 1889
Former Names: None
Nickname: 'White Tigers'
Ground: Treyew Road, Truro   TR1 2TH
Record Attendance: 2,637 (31st March 2007)
Colours: All Red shirts and shorts

Telephone Nº: (01872) 225400
Fax Number: (01872) 225402
Ground Capacity: 3,200
Seating Capacity: 1,600
Web Site: www.trurocityfc.net

GENERAL INFORMATION

Car Parking: At the ground
Coach Parking: At the ground
Nearest Railway Station: Truro (½ mile)
Club Shop: None

GROUND INFORMATION

Away Supporters' Entrances & Sections:
No usual segregation

ADMISSION INFO (2016/2017 PRICES)

Adult Standing: £13.00
Adult Seating: £13.00
Concessionary Standing: £10.00
Concessionary Seating: £10.00
Under-18s and Students Standing: £5.00
Under-18s and Students Seating: £5.00
Under-12s Standing: Free with a paying adult
Under-12s Seating: Free with a paying adult

DISABLED INFORMATION

Wheelchairs: Accommodated
Helpers: Admitted
Prices: Normal prices apply for the disabled and helpers
Disabled Toilets: Available
Contact: (01872) 225400   (Bookings are not necessary)

Travelling Supporters' Information:
Routes: From the North or East: Take the A30 to the A390 (from the North) or travel straight on the A390 (from the East) to Truro. Continue on the A390 and pass through Truro. The ground is located just to the South West of Truro on the left hand side of the A390 just before the County Hall; From the West: Take the A390 to Truro. The ground is on the right hand side of the road shortly after crossing the railway line and passing the County Hall; From the South: Take the A39 to Truro. At the junction with the A390 turn left onto Green Lane and the ground is on the left hand side of the road after approximately ½ mile.

WEALDSTONE FC

Photo courtesy of Steve Foster/Wealdstone FC

Founded: 1899
Former Names: None
Nickname: 'The Stones' or 'The Royals'
Ground: Grosvenor Vale, Ruislip   HA4 6JQ
Record Attendance: 1,638 (vs Rotherham United)
Colours: Royal Blue shirts with White shorts

Telephone Nº: (01895) 637487
Fax Number: (020) 8907-4421
Ground Capacity: 3,607
Seating Capacity: 329
Web site: www.wealdstone-fc.com

GENERAL INFORMATION
Car Parking: 100 spaces available at the ground
Coach Parking: Available outside the ground
Nearest Mainline Station: West Ruislip (1 mile)
Nearest Tube Station: Ruislip (½ mile)
Club Shop: Yes
Opening Times: Orders through the post only
Telephone Nº: –

GROUND INFORMATION
Away Supporters' Entrances & Sections:
No usual segregation

ADMISSION INFO (2016/2017 PRICES)
Adult Standing: £13.00
Adult Seating: £13.00
Concessionary Standing: £8.00
Concessionary Seating: £8.00
Under-18s Standing/Seating: £3.00
Note: Under-12s are admitted free of charge when accompanied by a paying adult

DISABLED INFORMATION
Wheelchairs: Accommodated
Helpers: Admitted
Prices: Normal prices apply
Disabled Toilets: Available
Contact: (01895) 637487

Travelling Supporters' Information:
Routes: Exit the M25 at Junction 16 and take the A40 towards Uxbridge. At the Polish War Memorial Junction with the A4180, follow the Ruislip signs (West End Road). After about 1½ miles, turn right into Grosvenor Vale for the ground.

WELLING UNITED FC

Founded: 1963
Former Names: None
Nickname: 'The Wings'
Ground: Park View Road Ground, Welling, Kent, DA16 1SY
Record Attendance: 4,020 (1989/90)
Pitch Size: 112 × 72 yards

Colours: Shirts are Red with White facings, Red shorts
Telephone Nº: (0208) 301-1196
Daytime Phone Nº: (0208) 301-1196
Fax Number: (0208) 301-5676
Ground Capacity: 4,000
Seating Capacity: 500
Web site: www.wellingunited.com

GENERAL INFORMATION

Car Parking: Street parking only
Coach Parking: Outside of the ground
Nearest Railway Station: Welling (¾ mile)
Nearest Bus Station: Bexleyheath
Club Shop: At the ground
Opening Times: Matchdays only
Telephone Nº: (0208) 301-1196

GROUND INFORMATION

Away Supporters' Entrances & Sections:
Accommodation in the Danson Park End

ADMISSION INFO (2016/2017 PRICES)

Adult Standing: £15.00
Adult Seating: £16.00
Concessionary Standing: £9.00 – £10.00
Concessionary Seating: £10.00 – £11.00
Under-12s Standing: Free with a paying adult
Under-12s Seating: £1.00 with a paying adult

DISABLED INFORMATION

Wheelchairs: Accommodated at the side of the Main Stand
Helpers: Admitted
Prices: £7.50 for the disabled. Helpers pay normal prices
Disabled Toilets: Yes
Contact: (0208) 301-1196 (Bookings are not necessary)

Travelling Supporters' Information:
Routes: Take the A2 (Rochester Way) from London, then the A221 Northwards (Danson Road) to Bexleyheath. At the end turn left towards Welling along Park View Road and the ground is on the left.

WESTON-SUPER-MARE FC

Founded: 1899
Former Names: Christ Church Old Boys FC
Nickname: 'Seagulls'
Ground: Woodspring Stadium, Winterstoke Road, Weston-super-Mare BS24 9AA
Record Attendance: 2,623 (vs Woking in F.A. Cup)
Pitch Size: 110 × 70 yards

Colours: White shirts with Black shorts
Telephone Nº: (01934) 621618
Fax Number: (01934) 622704
Ground Capacity: 3,071
Seating Capacity: 320
Web site: www.westonsmareafc.co.uk
E-mail: enquiries@wsmafc.co.uk

GENERAL INFORMATION
Car Parking: 140 spaces available at the ground
Coach Parking: At the ground
Nearest Railway Station: Weston-super-Mare (1½ miles)
Nearest Bus Station: Weston-super-Mare (1½ miles)
Club Shop: At the ground
Opening Times: Matchdays only
Telephone Nº: (01934) 621618

GROUND INFORMATION
Away Supporters' Entrances & Sections:
No usual segregation

ADMISSION INFO (2016/2017 PRICES)
Adult Standing/Seating: £10.00
Concessionary Standing/Seating: £7.00
Students and Under-24s Standing/Seating: £7.00
Note: Under-8s are admitted free of charge when accompanied by a paying adult or senior citizen. Under-16s are admitted for £2.00 with a paying adult or senior citizen.

DISABLED INFORMATION
Wheelchairs: Accommodated in a special disabled section
Helpers: Admitted
Prices: Normal prices apply
Disabled Toilets: Two available
Contact: (01934) 621618   (Bookings are not necessary)

Travelling Supporters' Information:
Routes: Exit the M5 at Junction 21 and follow the dual carriageway (A370) to the 4th roundabout (Asda Winterstoke). Turn left, go over the mini-roundabout and continue for 800 yards. The ground is on the right.

WHITEHAWK FC

Founded: 1945
Former Names: Whitehawk & Manor Farm Old Boys
Nickname: 'The Hawks'
Ground: The Enclosed Ground, East Brighton Park, Wilson Avenue, Brighton BN2 5TS
Record Attendance: 2,100 (1988/89 season)

Colours: Red shirts and shorts
Telephone Nº: (01273) 609736
Ground Capacity: 3,000
Seating Capacity: 200
Web Site: www.whitehawkfc.co.uk

GENERAL INFORMATION

Car Parking: At the ground
Coach Parking: At the ground
Nearest Railway Station: London Road (3¼ miles)
Club Shop: Online sales only
Opening Times: –
Telephone Nº: –

GROUND INFORMATION

Away Supporters' Entrances & Sections:
No usual segregation

ADMISSION INFO (2016/2017 PRICES)

Adult Standing: £12.00
Adult Seating: £12.00
Concessionary Standing: £7.00
Concessionary Seating: £7.00

DISABLED INFORMATION

Wheelchairs: Accommodated
Helpers: Admitted
Prices: Concessionary prices are charged for the disabled and helpers
Disabled Toilets: None
Contact: (01273) 609736 (Bookings are not necessary)

Travelling Supporters' Information:
Routes: Take the M23/A23 to the junction with the A27 on the outskirts of Brighton then follow the A27 towards Lewes. After passing Sussex University on the left, take the slip road onto the B2123 (signposted Falmer, Rottingdean) and continue for approximately 2 miles before turning right at the traffic lights into Warren Road by the Downs Hotel. Continue for approximately 1 mile then turn left at the traffic lights into Wilson Avenue. After 1¼ miles, turn left at the foot of the hill into East Brighton Park.

Home \ Away	Aldershot Town	Altrincham	Barrow	Boreham Wood	Braintree Town	Bromley	Cheltenham Town	Chester	Dover Athletic	Eastleigh	FC Halifax Town	Forest Green Rovers	Gateshead	Grimsby Town	Guiseley	Kidderminster Harriers	Lincoln City	Macclesfield Town	Southport	Torquay United	Tranmere Rovers	Welling United	Woking	Wrexham
Aldershot Town	■	2-0	0-1	1-2	2-1	1-1	0-2	3-1	1-1	1-2	3-2	0-3	1-2	3-4	1-0	1-0	1-2	0-3	1-2	0-0	0-0	1-0	0-1	0-1
Altrincham	4-0	■	1-0	1-0	0-4	0-0	2-1	0-3	1-2	1-1	1-3	0-1	2-3	2-1	1-1	2-2	3-3	0-0	1-1	1-1	2-1	5-0	3-1	1-1
Barrow	1-3	3-2	■	0-0	2-0	1-1	1-2	3-2	2-1	1-0	4-1	2-2	0-0	1-3	1-1	1-1	1-0	1-1	1-0	4-0	3-4	1-1	2-1	2-0
Boreham Wood	0-1	0-1	0-2	■	1-0	2-3	0-0	0-0	3-0	1-1	3-1	0-1	2-3	1-3	1-0	0-2	1-1	0-0	0-2	0-1	0-0	2-0	1-1	0-1
Braintree Town	1-2	3-0	1-1	0-2	■	1-0	1-0	2-0	1-0	2-0	1-1	0-0	0-0	0-1	2-1	1-3	1-0	1-0	0-0	0-0	1-1	0-0	1-0	1-0
Bromley	1-3	1-3	5-0	1-2	1-2	■	1-2	3-0	1-1	2-2	1-0	2-2	3-0	1-2	2-0	3-2	2-0	1-0	0-0	0-2	0-1	2-0	2-1	3-1
Cheltenham Town	0-0	1-0	2-1	4-1	1-1	4-1	■	3-1	3-2	1-1	2-0	1-1	0-0	3-1	5-0	2-0	3-1	2-0	3-0	1-0	0-1	2-0	4-0	2-1
Chester	8-2	1-1	1-2	2-2	1-0	1-1	1-1	■	1-1	1-0	2-1	1-2	4-2	1-1	1-1	3-1	2-3	0-2	0-0	4-1	0-1	4-0	1-2	3-2
Dover Athletic	5-2	2-1	3-1	2-1	0-0	2-3	1-2	0-0	■	1-2	1-0	0-1	4-0	1-1	0-0	3-2	4-1	2-1	1-2	5-0	0-0	2-1	2-0	2-1
Eastleigh	1-1	2-0	3-1	1-0	0-2	2-0	1-0	1-0	2-5	■	2-1	3-2	1-2	0-1	1-1	3-1	1-1	1-0	1-0	3-2	1-1	0-0	2-1	1-1
FC Halifax Town	0-2	1-0	3-1	3-2	3-6	2-2	1-7	0-1	4-2	0-0	■	0-2	1-1	4-2	1-1	1-1	2-2	1-1	2-2	2-3	1-1	1-1	0-3	2-0
Forest Green Rovers	0-0	2-0	4-0	1-0	1-0	2-1	2-2	2-1	3-1	2-1	0-1	■	0-1	0-1	3-0	3-0	3-1	2-1	3-1	0-2	1-0	1-2	1-2	0-0
Gateshead	3-2	2-2	1-1	2-1	2-3	3-1	1-1	1-0	2-3	2-1	1-4	0-1	■	1-0	3-0	1-1	2-0	0-3	0-1	1-2	1-4	1-2	1-5	2-1
Grimsby Town	4-1	5-0	4-1	0-0	0-1	4-1	0-1	1-2	1-0	0-0	7-0	1-1	2-1	■	1-1	1-0	2-0	0-2	1-0	2-2	1-1	3-1	3-1	1-0
Guiseley	0-4	1-0	3-1	1-1	1-1	2-0	0-2	3-3	0-1	1-4	0-1	0-2	2-2	1-2	■	1-0	0-1	0-3	1-1	4-3	2-2	2-0	4-4	3-1
Kidderminster Harriers	2-0	1-1	0-0	1-1	0-1	0-1	1-2	2-2	1-1	3-2	1-0	0-2	2-2	0-1	2-2	■	0-2	3-1	0-1	2-2	0-1	0-1	1-0	1-3
Lincoln City	2-0	1-1	2-2	3-1	2-0	0-1	1-1	2-1	2-3	3-0	0-1	0-1	1-1	1-1	1-0	1-2	■	5-3	3-1	2-0	1-0	1-1	2-3	1-1
Macclesfield Town	0-2	3-0	1-2	0-0	3-1	2-0	0-1	1-2	0-0	1-2	0-1	4-1	1-0	2-1	1-0	2-1	1-1	■	0-0	1-2	1-2	2-1	2-1	0-0
Southport	1-1	3-0	2-1	0-3	1-1	5-3	0-4	1-2	0-0	0-4	1-2	0-2	2-0	3-4	2-2	3-1	2-0	1-1	■	0-1	2-2	3-3	2-2	3-2
Torquay United	0-2	2-0	2-2	1-2	0-0	3-7	0-3	2-0	2-3	0-1	0-0	4-1	0-2	1-1	1-1	3-2	1-3	1-0	1-0	■	0-1	2-0	0-1	0-1
Tranmere Rovers	3-1	1-0	0-1	0-2	1-2	4-0	0-1	2-0	0-1	1-2	1-0	1-1	3-1	1-0	2-1	2-2	3-2	0-1	1-0	2-1	■	1-2	1-0	1-2
Welling United	0-1	1-1	1-2	0-3	1-2	1-2	1-1	2-1	1-2	2-2	2-0	1-1	0-4	1-0	1-2	2-1	0-1	0-1	1-1	1-1	1-2	■	2-1	0-2
Woking	2-1	2-0	2-2	0-0	1-1	2-0	0-1	5-2	0-1	2-1	1-1	2-1	1-1	1-3	0-1	1-1	3-1	2-5	1-2	2-2	4-1	2-0	■	0-1
Wrexham	3-0	3-1	4-1	1-0	2-3	2-0	2-1	3-0	0-1	2-3	3-1	2-2	4-0	0-0	3-3	2-0	3-1	2-3	0-1	3-1	2-2	1-0	1-3	■

Football Conference National

Season 2015/2016

Team	P	W	D	L	F	A	Pts
Cheltenham Town	46	30	11	5	87	30	101
Forest Green Rovers	46	26	11	9	69	41	89
Braintree Town	46	23	12	11	56	38	81
Grimsby Town	46	22	14	10	82	45	80
Dover Athletic	46	23	11	12	75	53	80
Tranmere Rovers	46	22	12	12	61	44	78
Eastleigh	46	21	12	13	64	53	75
Wrexham	46	20	9	17	71	56	69
Gateshead	46	19	10	17	59	70	67
Macclesfield Town	46	19	9	18	60	48	66
Barrow	46	17	14	15	64	71	65
Woking	46	17	10	19	71	68	61
Lincoln City	46	16	13	17	69	68	61
Bromley	46	17	9	20	67	72	60
Aldershot Town	46	16	8	22	54	72	56
Southport	46	14	13	19	52	65	55
Chester	46	14	12	20	67	71	54
Torquay United	46	13	12	21	54	76	51
Boreham Wood	46	12	14	20	44	49	50
Guiseley	46	11	16	19	47	70	49
FC Halifax Town	46	12	12	22	55	82	48
Altrincham	46	10	14	22	48	73	44
Kidderminster Harriers	46	9	13	24	49	70	40
Welling United	46	8	11	27	35	73	35

Promotion Play-offs

Dover Athletic 0   Forest Green Rovers 1
Grimsby Town 0   Braintree Town 1

Forest Green Rovers 1   Dover Athletic 1
Forest Green Rovers won 2-1 on aggregate.
Braintree Town 0   Grimsby Town .... 2 (aet)
Grimsby Town won 2-1 on aggregate.

Forest Green Rovers 1   Grimsby Town 3

Promoted: Cheltenham Town and Grimsby Town

Relegated: FC Halifax Town, Altrincham, Kidderminster Harriers and Welling United

National League North 2015/2016 Season

	AFC Fylde	AFC Telford United	Alfreton Town	Boston United	Brackley Town	Bradford Park Avenue	Chorley	Corby Town	Curzon Ashton	FC United of Manchester	Gainsborough Trinity	Gloucester City	Harrogate Town	Hednesford Town	Lowestoft Town	North Ferriby United	Nuneaton Town	Solihull Moors	Stalybridge Celtic	Stockport County	Tamworth	Worcester City
AFC Fylde		1-0	0-1	5-2	2-2	1-0	1-0	2-1	1-2	4-0	2-2	1-0	2-1	2-0	1-0	2-3	2-2	1-2	5-0	2-3	2-2	2-3
AFC Telford United	1-2		1-1	2-2	2-0	3-1	2-0	3-0	0-0	5-1	0-2	0-1	0-4	1-3	1-0	1-1	1-5	0-3	2-0	0-1	1-0	2-0
Alfreton Town	1-2	2-3		1-2	1-1	0-1	1-0	1-1	2-2	0-1	1-0	1-1	3-2	4-0	0-1	0-1	2-2	2-2	1-3	0-3	1-0	2-1
Boston United	0-3	1-0	2-1		1-2	3-0	1-2	2-0	2-1	3-1	1-0	1-0	3-3	3-1	4-1	1-2	2-1	1-4	0-3	4-0	1-1	1-1
Brackley Town	0-0	0-0	1-4	1-3		0-0	1-1	1-2	2-0	4-0	3-2	1-0	1-0	1-1	2-2	2-4	2-3	0-1	2-3	0-1	1-0	2-0
Bradford Park Avenue	1-2	1-0	2-2	1-2	1-0		1-0	1-0	4-2	3-1	1-4	1-1	3-1	1-1	3-0	4-4	2-3	1-1	3-1	0-0	0-2	3-1
Chorley	3-2	2-1	1-2	2-0	1-0	2-2		3-0	2-0	3-0	3-1	0-1	0-1	2-2	2-0	2-3	2-3	2-2	0-0	1-0	1-1	2-0
Corby Town	1-2	3-2	2-3	2-3	1-1	2-0	2-2		0-4	2-3	1-2	3-1	0-3	0-0	3-5	1-4	1-3	1-3	0-3	0-4	2-0	0-3
Curzon Ashton	0-2	1-0	0-2	0-2	1-1	2-1	4-2	2-2		0-0	3-0	1-1	1-2	3-2	4-1	0-3	1-0	1-3	0-0	0-0	2-0	3-1
FC United of Manchester	1-2	1-3	1-3	1-2	3-2	2-1	2-0	1-0	3-3		1-2	1-2	4-3	1-1	6-1	3-2	3-2	2-2	0-1	1-2	1-1	0-2
Gainsborough Trinity	0-2	1-1	1-1	1-0	1-0	0-1	2-1	1-1	0-2	0-1		3-3	2-1	3-1	1-1	2-0	1-0	1-6	3-1	0-1	0-2	1-1
Gloucester City	1-3	1-0	1-1	1-0	0-0	1-3	1-1	1-0	3-1	1-0	0-2		0-1	2-2	0-1	3-2	0-1	0-2	3-0	0-0	1-2	0-1
Harrogate Town	2-2	0-1	1-2	0-0	1-0	1-2	2-4	5-0	1-1	5-0	3-1	0-0		2-1	4-0	3-3	0-3	6-0	2-1	2-1	0-0	1-0
Hednesford Town	0-1	2-0	3-3	3-2	0-2	0-0	1-3	3-3	0-3	0-3	0-2	2-2	2-3		2-1	1-1	2-4	0-0	2-1	1-2	2-1	0-1
Lowestoft Town	3-1	3-0	1-0	3-0	1-2	3-0	2-0	2-2	0-0	1-4	1-0	1-1	1-2	0-0		0-3	0-1	2-2	0-2	2-2	0-4	2-1
North Ferriby United	3-0	2-0	0-1	4-3	2-1	1-0	4-0	5-0	0-0	1-0	4-0	3-0	0-1	1-1	0-0		1-2	1-1	1-0	2-0	3-1	3-3
Nuneaton Town	1-1	0-0	2-0	1-3	1-0	1-0	2-2	0-0	0-1	2-2	2-0	0-1	0-0	3-0	1-0	3-1		0-1	3-3	1-1	3-0	1-1
Solihull Moors	3-0	2-1	2-1	0-1	3-0	2-1	0-2	4-1	2-0	1-2	3-2	0-0	1-0	1-2	2-1	1-3	3-1		4-1	1-0	1-2	3-0
Stalybridge Celtic	1-1	5-5	1-1	0-5	3-1	1-1	0-1	2-3	1-1	1-1	0-0	1-0	0-1	4-2	3-1	2-0	2-5	1-3		1-1	3-5	3-1
Stockport County	0-4	0-1	1-0	2-1	1-1	2-0	1-3	2-2	0-0	1-2	2-0	3-0	1-2	3-0	0-2	1-1	1-1	2-4	0-3		1-1	0-0
Tamworth	3-1	2-1	1-2	1-2	1-2	0-0	2-1	0-0	2-1	1-1	2-0	2-2	1-0	1-0	1-1	1-0	1-1	1-1	1-1	1-1		3-0
Worcester City	2-2	3-0	1-1	2-1	0-0	3-1	2-3	1-2	2-2	0-0	2-0	1-2	0-0	1-4	2-1	2-0	0-1	2-2	5-0	2-3	1-2	

Football Conference North

Season 2015/2016

Solihull Moors	42	25	10	7	84	48	85
North Ferriby United	42	22	10	10	82	49	76
AFC Fylde	42	22	9	11	76	53	75
Harrogate Town	42	21	9	12	73	46	72
Boston United	42	22	5	15	73	60	71
Nuneaton Town	42	20	13	9	71	46	70
Tamworth	42	16	15	11	55	45	63
Chorley	42	18	9	15	64	55	63
Stockport County	42	15	14	13	50	49	59
Alfreton Town	42	15	13	14	58	54	58
Curzon Ashton	42	14	15	13	55	52	57
Stalybridge Celtic	42	14	11	17	62	75	53
FC United of Manchester	42	15	8	19	60	75	53
Bradford Park Avenue	42	13	11	18	51	59	50
Gloucester City	42	12	14	16	39	49	50
Gainsborough Trinity	42	14	8	20	46	62	50
Worcester City	42	12	12	18	55	61	48
AFC Telford United	42	13	8	21	47	60	47
Brackley Town	42	11	13	18	45	54	46
Lowestoft Town	42	12	10	20	48	69	46
Hednesford Town	42	8	14	20	50	77	38
Corby Town	42	7	11	24	47	93	32

Nuneaton Town had 3 points deducted for fielding an ineligible player

Promotion Play-offs North

Boston United 2   North Ferriby United 0
Harrogate Town 0   AFC Fylde 1

North Ferriby United 3   Boston United 0
North Ferriby United won 3-2 on aggregate.
AFC Fylde 1   Harrogate Town 1
AFC Fylde won 2-1 on aggregate

North Ferriby United 2   AFC Fylde .... 1 (aet)

Promoted: Barrow and AFC Fylde

Relegated: Lowestoft Town, Hednesford Town and Corby Town

National League South 2015/2016	Basingstoke Town	Bath City	Bishop's Stortford	Chelmsford City	Concord Rangers	Dartford	Eastbourne Borough	Ebbsfleet United	Gosport Borough	Havant & Waterlooville	Hayes & Yeading United	Hemel Hempstead Town	Maidenhead United	Maidstone United	Margate	Oxford City	St Albans City	Sutton United	Truro City	Wealdstone	Weston-super-Mare	Whitehawk
Basingstoke Town		1-2	1-1	1-2	0-2	0-1	1-5	1-2	0-1	1-1	1-0	2-0	2-1	0-1	0-0	2-0	2-2	1-2	2-0	1-1	2-2	3-1
Bath City	0-0		2-2	2-0	0-1	0-0	1-0	1-1	0-1	5-0	2-3	1-1	2-1	0-2	2-0	1-3	1-0	1-3	0-3	2-1	2-1	0-3
Bishop's Stortford	1-2	3-2		1-2	3-2	1-2	1-1	1-2	2-0	3-0	0-0	1-0	0-2	0-1	4-1	3-0	2-1	0-2	0-3	2-1	0-1	2-1
Chelmsford City	0-2	3-1	4-1		5-2	0-1	0-3	0-0	6-1	2-2	4-0	0-1	4-1	3-0	2-3	0-4	2-1	0-2	1-2	0-2	2-3	4-3
Concord Rangers	5-0	1-2	2-2	1-0		2-3	4-1	0-0	0-0	0-1	0-3	0-3	2-0	1-2	2-1	0-2	1-2	0-3	1-2	2-2	4-1	1-2
Dartford	0-0	4-1	3-1	1-1	1-2		1-0	0-1	2-3	4-2	2-0	2-2	2-0	1-1	1-1	2-2	2-0	2-2	0-1	1-2	2-1	2-4
Eastbourne Borough	1-2	5-2	0-1	2-0	0-0	1-1		1-2	3-0	2-2	2-0	2-3	1-2	1-0	1-4	1-1	1-0	1-1	0-0	3-0	3-3	1-1
Ebbsfleet United	1-0	0-1	4-2	3-1	4-2	1-1	4-2		2-0	2-2	0-0	6-0	3-1	0-1	1-2	1-1	1-0	1-0	0-0	2-3	2-1	2-2
Gosport Borough	3-2	3-1	0-0	2-1	2-3	1-3	3-1	1-2		2-1	2-5	2-6	2-1	0-0	1-2	0-0	0-0	0-2	3-1	1-1	1-0	2-2
Havant & Waterlooville	1-0	1-1	2-1	0-1	2-1	2-0	4-0	1-4	1-3		1-0	1-2	3-1	2-1	2-0	2-1	1-1	0-2	0-0	1-2	1-1	2-3
Hayes & Yeading United	3-0	0-3	0-2	0-5	2-2	2-2	4-4	0-5	0-0	0-0		1-1	2-5	1-0	0-2	2-1	1-3	1-3	2-2	0-0	1-1	3-4
Hemel Hempstead Town	2-2	1-1	1-2	1-1	1-2	1-0	1-0	1-2	1-0	2-0	4-0		0-1	0-1	1-2	3-1	2-2	2-2	2-1	2-2	5-5	0-3
Maidenhead United	4-3	3-1	4-1	1-0	2-2	2-1	2-0	0-0	0-0	2-2	2-1	2-3		0-2	3-1	2-1	0-1	1-1	0-0	1-1	2-0	3-0
Maidstone United	3-1	1-0	1-1	0-1	2-2	1-2	2-1	0-2	2-1	1-0	3-1	2-1	1-2		2-1	0-1	1-0	1-2	2-1	1-0	3-1	0-1
Margate	2-1	1-1	1-1	4-1	0-1	0-2	0-1	0-2	1-0	4-1	1-2	4-3	3-2	1-0		0-2	0-1	0-4	1-1	0-0	0-2	2-6
Oxford City	2-2	1-1	3-1	2-2	5-1	2-1	2-2	1-1	1-2	1-3	2-2	0-2	0-0	2-3	1-1		4-1	0-1	1-2	3-2	3-0	0-0
St Albans City	3-0	0-1	1-1	1-1	2-2	4-0	3-1	0-2	1-3	6-0	1-1	2-2	3-2	1-2	3-0	1-3		0-3	0-1	1-0	2-1	6-0
Sutton United	2-0	1-1	2-0	2-0	2-2	2-0	2-1	2-0	1-0	3-0	0-1	2-2	2-2	0-2	4-1	1-1	5-0		2-2	5-2	0-0	2-2
Truro City	2-0	3-1	0-1	1-0	2-1	3-0	1-0	1-1	2-2	3-0	0-2	4-2	4-4	1-3	2-1	0-6	2-0	0-2		1-2	1-3	1-1
Wealdstone	4-4	2-0	3-1	0-0	1-2	2-1	0-1	1-2	1-1	3-2	3-0	0-0	0-0	2-2	4-1	2-2	1-1	0-2	4-4		2-3	2-2
Weston-super-Mare	2-1	1-1	1-1	0-3	0-3	2-1	1-2	2-1	0-4	3-2	0-2	2-4	2-0	1-2	1-0	5-2	4-1	0-2	2-2	1-2		1-2
Whitehawk	1-0	0-1	2-3	4-2	0-2	0-1	1-2	0-1	3-0	1-1	1-3	0-1	3-2	1-0	2-2	2-0	6-0	2-0	0-0	3-0	0-2	

Football Conference South

Season 2015/2016

Sutton United	42	26	12	4	83	32	90
Ebbsfleet United	42	24	12	6	73	36	84
Maidstone United	42	24	5	13	55	40	77
Truro City	42	17	14	11	62	55	65
Whitehawk	42	18	10	14	75	62	64
Hemel Hempstead Town	42	16	13	13	72	66	61
Maidenhead United	42	16	11	15	66	62	59
Dartford	42	16	11	15	58	56	59
Gosport Borough	42	15	11	16	53	63	56
Concord Rangers	42	15	10	17	66	68	55
Bishop's Stortford	42	15	10	17	56	63	55
Oxford City	42	13	15	14	70	60	54
Wealdstone	42	12	17	13	63	64	53
Bath City	42	14	11	17	50	61	53
Chelmsford City	42	15	7	20	66	64	52
Weston-super-Mare	42	14	9	19	63	76	51
Eastbourne Borough	42	13	11	18	60	63	50
St. Albans City	42	13	10	19	58	65	49
Margate	42	13	8	21	51	73	47
Havant & Waterlooville	42	12	11	19	52	75	47
Hayes & Yeading United	42	11	13	18	51	76	46
Basingstoke Town	42	9	11	22	46	69	38

Promotion Play-offs South

Truro City 0   Maidstone United 2
Whitehawk 1   Ebbsfleet United 2

Maidstone United 1   Truro City 0
Maidstone United won 3-0 on aggregate.
Ebbsfleet United 1   Whitehawk .... 2 (aet)
Aggregate 3-3. Ebbsfleet United won 3-2 on penalties.

Ebbsfleet United 2   Maidstone United .... 2 (aet)
Maidstone United won 4-3 on aggregate

Promoted: Sutton United and Maidstone United

Relegated: Havant & Waterlooville, Hayes & Yeading United and Basingstoke Town

Northern Premier League Premier Division 2015/2016 Season

Home \ Away	Ashton United	Barwell	Blyth Spartans	Buxton	Colwyn Bay	Darlington 1883	Frickley Athletic	Grantham Town	Halesowen Town	Hyde United	Ilkeston Town	Marine	Matlock Town	Mickleover Sports	Nantwich Town	Ramsbottom United	Rushall Olympic	Salford City	Skelmersdale United	Stamford	Stourbridge	Sutton Coldfield Town	Whitby Town	Workington
Ashton United	■	2-0	0-2	3-1	1-2	1-2	2-0	2-0	3-0	3-0	2-1	3-2	4-4	0-0	4-2	6-0	2-3	0-3	5-0	1-0	2-3	3-0	2-0	0-1
Barwell	0-1	■	0-1	1-0	3-0	2-1	1-0	3-1	6-0	2-0	4-0	1-1	4-0	2-4	0-4	2-1	2-3	0-1	3-1	0-1	3-1	2-0	2-1	0-1
Blyth Spartans	1-1	4-0	■	1-0	3-0	0-1	2-3	1-0	0-1	3-0	1-0	1-2	1-0	4-0	1-1	5-0	3-0	2-1	1-2	4-3	4-3	1-2	3-2	3-0
Buxton	2-1	5-1	0-4	■	2-0	2-0	0-2	3-0	1-1	2-1	3-1	2-3	3-0	4-1	3-1	2-1	1-2	0-2	2-1	3-1	2-3	2-2	3-2	0-2
Colwyn Bay	0-2	0-4	1-3	3-2	■	2-4	0-2	0-1	1-1	2-0	0-2	0-3	1-4	1-2	1-1	4-1	1-2	2-3	1-4	2-1	0-2	3-0	1-4	0-2
Darlington 1883	1-1	3-1	2-1	3-1	3-0	■	3-0	2-0	2-1	2-3	3-1	0-1	3-0	2-1	2-1	2-1	1-0	3-2	3-0	2-1	1-1	2-0	2-2	4-0
Frickley Athletic	0-0	1-0	2-3	5-1	1-0	3-1	■	3-1	1-2	3-0	1-1	0-1	1-2	2-0	1-0	3-0	0-2	0-1	3-0	3-1	2-1	3-1	2-2	1-1
Grantham Town	3-3	0-5	2-3	0-3	0-0	0-2	1-0	■	2-0	2-0	1-2	0-0	2-0	0-3	0-4	2-2	2-0	2-3	3-1	2-2	2-1	1-0	0-1	
Halesowen Town	1-2	1-1	0-1	1-1	1-0	0-3	1-1	3-0	■	1-1	2-0	1-0	3-2	1-1	1-1	2-1	1-3	0-1	2-1	1-3	2-0	2-2	0-0	2-0
Hyde United	0-4	1-0	0-4	2-1	3-2	1-3	1-1	2-2	0-1	■	1-3	0-2	2-2	0-1	0-4	5-0	2-2	1-2	1-1	7-1	0-2	1-2	2-1	0-4
Ilkeston	1-1	1-0	3-4	3-1	0-0	1-1	0-2	2-1	1-3	3-1	■	0-0	0-1	2-3	3-0	4-1	2-1	1-3	0-3	4-3	1-1	2-1	0-3	
Marine	0-0	1-2	0-2	1-2	2-2	0-1	1-1	1-1	0-3	2-3	3-1	■	2-1	3-3	1-2	3-0	1-1	0-2	2-2	1-1	3-1	2-1	2-1	1-2
Matlock Town	1-0	1-3	0-2	1-2	1-1	0-5	3-0	3-1	0-3	2-1	1-0	0-0	■	2-0	1-1	1-0	1-2	1-2	0-1	1-1	2-2	1-0	0-1	
Mickleover Sports	1-3	1-3	0-2	2-0	1-2	1-5	0-1	2-3	2-0	1-1	1-1	2-0		■	1-1	3-1	1-1	2-0	1-3	0-1			1-0	1-2
Nantwich Town	2-2	2-1	1-2	1-2	3-2	0-5	1-0	6-2	3-0	3-0	1-1	1-1	2-2	1-1	■	7-1	3-3	1-1	1-0	6-3	1-0	4-1	1-2	2-0
Ramsbottom United	0-2	1-3	0-0	0-1	2-2	0-3	0-2	2-2	0-2	1-4	4-0	1-1	0-3	1-1	1-4	■	2-1	0-4	0-3	1-1	1-2	0-1	4-1	1-1
Rushall Olympic	0-2	2-0	0-1	0-1	2-1	1-0	0-1	4-0	0-0	2-0	2-2	3-0	2-3	1-1	1-0	2-0	■	2-3	0-0	5-1	1-2	0-1	3-1	1-1
Salford City	3-1	7-0	0-1	2-0	2-2	3-4	2-2	5-0	3-1	0-1	2-0	0-0	2-2	1-1	1-1	4-0	1-3	■	4-0	1-0	0-1	2-0	0-0	5-3
Skelmersdale United	1-2	3-3	2-1	2-1	3-4	1-1	1-1	1-0	2-1	2-1	2-3	3-2	1-1	0-1	1-1	4-1	3-1		■	1-4	1-2	1-2	2-0	
Stamford	3-4	1-2	0-1	2-4	2-3	1-4	1-0	1-3	1-2	2-1	1-1	0-0	2-0	2-0	0-4	3-3	2-3	1-1	5-2	■	2-2	3-3	2-2	1-2
Stourbridge	1-2	2-3	3-0	3-0	1-2	1-0	1-1	1-1	3-2	5-1	1-2	2-4	4-1	2-1	4-3	2-3	2-2	1-2	3-1	2-0	■	2-0	2-0	0-0
Sutton Coldfield Town	0-1	1-5	1-0	0-0	5-0	0-1	2-2	2-0	3-0	0-0	4-2	2-2	2-0	1-3	2-2	2-1	0-2	0-3	2-0	2-3		■	1-0	0-2
Whitby Town	0-2	2-1	0-2	1-0	2-0	1-7	1-1	1-1	2-1	0-3	4-2	1-0	2-1	4-1	3-3	1-1	1-3	2-3	1-1	3-5	4-0	0-1	■	1-0
Workington	5-2	1-1	2-0	5-0	1-2	2-1	1-3	1-1	3-0	2-0	1-0	4-1	2-2	1-1	4-0	1-1	1-4	2-1	2-0	1-1	1-1	3-1		■

Evo-Stik League – Northern Premier Division

Season 2015/2016

Team	P	W	D	L	F	A	Pts
Darlington 1883	46	33	5	8	106	42	104
Blyth Spartans	46	32	3	11	89	41	99
Salford City	46	27	9	10	94	48	90
Ashton United	46	26	9	11	90	52	87
Workington	46	25	11	10	78	50	86
Stourbridge	46	25	9	12	90	63	84
Frickley Athletic	46	22	11	13	69	46	77
Nantwich Town	46	20	15	11	94	62	75
Barwell	46	23	4	19	82	66	73
Rushall Olympic	46	19	12	15	74	61	69
Buxton	46	21	4	21	71	74	67
Sutton Coldfield Town	46	17	11	18	59	66	62
Halesowen Town	46	17	11	18	53	63	62
Ilkeston	46	15	9	22	61	79	54
Marine	46	12	17	17	53	61	53
Skelmersdale United	46	14	11	21	66	82	53
Matlock Town	46	14	10	22	59	79	52
Grantham Town	46	13	12	21	51	85	51
Whitby Town	46	12	11	23	60	79	47
Mickleover Sports	46	11	13	22	50	74	46
Stamford	46	12	9	25	71	97	45
Hyde United	46	11	7	28	53	90	40
Colwyn Bay	46	10	8	28	51	95	38
Ramsbottom United	46	5	11	30	43	112	26

Promotion Play-offs

Blyth Spartans 3   Workington 4
Salford City 3   Ashton United .... 1 (aet)

Salford City 3   Workington 2

Promoted: Darlington 1883 and Salford City

Relegated: Stamford, Hyde United, Colwyn Bay and Ramsbottom United

Southern Football League Premier Division 2015/2016 Season

	Bedworth United	Bideford	Biggleswade Town	Cambridge City	Chesham United	Chippenham Town	Cirencester Town	Dorchester Town	Dunstable Town	Frome Town	Histon	Hitchin Town	Hungerford Town	Kettering Town	King's Lynn Town	Leamington	Merthyr Town	Paulton Rovers	Poole Town	Redditch United	Slough Town	St Neots Town	Stratford Town	Weymouth
Bedworth United		2-2	2-4	4-3	3-1	0-2	0-1	1-0	1-2	2-2	3-2	1-2	0-2	1-1	3-0	2-0	1-2	1-1	0-2	1-2	2-1	0-6	0-4	3-2
Bideford	2-1		0-0	1-1	0-0	0-1	1-1	2-3	0-0	2-0	0-5	0-0	1-2	2-0	0-5	1-1	0-1	0-1	1-2	0-5	2-1	4-4	1-1	0-2
Biggleswade Town	4-1	0-2		3-2	2-2	0-1	1-0	1-0	3-3	3-0	2-1	3-5	1-4	1-3	2-4	3-2	0-3	4-1	0-1	1-1	5-1	5-2	4-3	1-1
Cambridge City	4-2	2-0	2-2		1-0	0-3	1-2	0-3	1-1	2-1	1-2	0-1	3-1	0-4	1-3	1-2	1-0	2-0	1-2	0-2	4-2	1-4	2-0	1-0
Chesham United	4-2	3-1	1-1	1-3		1-0	1-3	3-4	5-1	5-1	2-0	1-1	2-2	0-3	2-0	3-0	0-1	3-1	3-0	1-1	3-1	2-0	1-0	
Chippenham Town	5-0	2-0	3-2	1-3	2-2		0-1	3-1	4-1	1-1	3-0	1-1	1-1	0-2	4-1	4-3	1-0	3-0	0-1	0-3	3-3	1-1	2-1	1-1
Cirencester Town	2-3	3-4	2-1	1-1	3-0	1-4		4-3	1-5	1-1	1-2	0-0	2-3	1-0	0-1	1-2	1-0	3-0	3-0	0-2	1-3	2-5	3-0	0-3
Dorchester Town	3-2	1-2	0-1	3-0	2-1	1-1	1-1		0-0	0-0	3-0	0-1	0-1	1-4	2-0	0-1	1-1	6-0	1-5	1-5	1-2	1-0	3-1	1-0
Dunstable Town	1-2	5-0	2-1	3-1	1-1	1-2	0-2	1-0		3-2	4-2	0-0	1-0	4-0	0-2	0-2	2-1	1-2	1-1	1-2	1-3	3-0	3-1	2-1
Frome Town	2-1	3-0	2-1	0-4	1-1	1-0	3-2	0-3	4-3		2-2	0-4	0-2	1-2	1-0	0-0	1-1	1-0	0-0	1-1	2-1	3-2	2-0	1-1
Histon	4-1	3-2	1-2	2-3	3-1	0-0	3-3	0-1	3-1	1-3		5-1	0-3	3-1	1-2	0-3	0-2	1-1	0-7	0-0	1-2	0-0	0-2	1-4
Hitchin Town	3-1	0-0	3-0	4-2	5-1	1-1	2-0	3-2	4-1	1-2	3-2		2-1	2-1	2-0	2-2	2-0	0-0	0-0	1-0	3-1	2-0	2-3	1-0
Hungerford Town	5-1	2-0	1-0	2-0	3-1	1-0	1-2	2-3	2-3	4-0	1-0	1-1		2-1	2-1	1-2	1-0	3-1	0-0	0-0	1-0	3-3	0-0	0-1
Kettering Town	0-1	7-0	2-1	0-0	3-0	1-2	4-3	3-0	3-1	1-1	5-4	1-1	2-1		2-1	1-1	3-2	2-0	1-0	0-0	1-1	1-1	3-1	0-1
King's Lynn Town	3-0	0-1	2-1	1-0	2-0	2-0	2-0	1-2	1-1	1-0	4-2	1-0	0-1	0-3		0-1	2-3	0-0	3-2	1-0	2-1	1-1	2-1	0-0
Leamington	0-0	2-1	2-1	1-2	1-0	2-2	2-0	3-0	1-0	2-0	2-1	0-1	0-0	3-2	1-1		1-0	2-0	1-0	0-1	3-0	2-2	1-0	0-0
Merthyr Town	2-2	3-0	1-2	2-1	1-2	2-0	0-1	2-4	1-3	1-1	3-0	5-1	4-1	1-1	2-0	0-2		1-1	1-1	2-1	2-0	1-1	3-0	1-3
Paulton Rovers	0-0	0-0	3-2	2-1	2-0	0-1	1-4	1-1	1-2	2-1	0-2	2-1	0-0	1-3	1-1	1-2			0-4	0-5	3-3	2-5	2-1	1-1
Poole Town	5-0	3-0	2-2	2-1	3-0	1-3	3-0	0-0	3-0	5-0	1-0	0-0	1-0	1-1	0-0	1-0	2-2	2-1		2-1	3-3	3-0	1-2	2-0
Redditch United	8-1	4-1	2-2	0-0	1-0	6-2	0-1	2-0	0-0	1-1	1-0	3-2	2-2	2-1	2-0	0-0	3-1	1-1	0-0		1-0	1-1	3-2	1-1
Slough Town	1-2	2-1	2-0	3-1	0-1	1-0	1-0	1-2	1-0	0-0	7-1	1-0	0-2	1-3	2-0	1-3	3-1	2-1	1-3	0-2		2-2	2-4	0-0
St Neots Town	2-2	3-1	2-0	1-1	2-4	0-4	1-2	1-0	1-0	2-2	1-1	1-2	0-2	0-1	0-1	1-2	1-0	2-3	1-3	0-0			2-2	1-1
Stratford Town	2-0	0-0	3-0	5-2	1-1	1-1	2-1	1-2	0-0	0-1	1-2	1-1	0-2	2-1	1-1	0-1	0-3	4-0	0-1	1-0	1-1	2-1		1-1
Weymouth	1-0	1-0	0-1	1-0	1-4	1-1	3-1	2-2	0-0	2-0	1-0	0-2	2-1	3-2	2-0	1-0	3-0	4-1	0-1	2-0	6-1	1-1	2-1	

Evo-Stik Southern Premier
Premier Division

Season 2015/2016

Team	P	W	D	L	F	A	Pts
Poole Town	46	27	12	7	86	35	93
Redditch United	46	24	15	7	82	37	84
Hitchin Town	46	24	12	10	78	50	84
Hungerford Town	46	24	11	11	73	43	83
Leamington	46	23	12	11	59	38	81
Kettering Town	46	24	8	14	83	53	80
Weymouth	46	21	14	11	63	39	77
Chippenham Town	46	21	13	12	76	53	76
King's Lynn Town	46	21	7	18	58	54	70
Merthyr Town	46	19	9	18	69	58	66
Chesham United	46	18	10	18	72	70	64
Dunstable Town	46	17	11	18	68	68	62
Dorchester Town	46	18	8	20	67	69	62
Biggleswade Town	46	17	9	20	76	82	60
Cirencester Town	46	18	6	22	67	76	60
Frome Town	46	14	16	16	51	73	58
Slough Town	46	16	9	21	67	77	57
Cambridge City	46	15	7	24	63	80	52
Stratford Town	46	13	11	22	59	68	50
St Neots Town	46	10	18	18	69	78	48
Bedworth United	46	12	8	26	58	107	44
Histon	46	11	7	28	63	98	40
Bideford	46	8	13	25	38	88	37
Paulton Rovers	46	8	12	26	38	89	36

Redditch United had 3 points deducted for fielding ineligible players

Promotion Play-offs

Hitchin Town 2   Hungerford Town 3
Redditch United 1   Leamington .... 1 (aet)
Leamington won 3-1 on penalties

Hungerford Town 2   Leamington 1

Promoted: Poole Town and Hungerford Town
Relegated: Bedworth, Histon, Bideford and Paulton Rovers

Isthmian League Premier Division 2015/2016 Season

	Billericay Town	Bognor Regis Town	Brentwood Town	Burgess Hill Town	Canvey Island	Dulwich Hamlet	East Thurrock United	Enfield Town	Farnborough	Grays Athletic	Hampton & Richmond Borough	Harrow Borough	Hendon	Kingstonian	Leatherhead	Leiston	Lewes	Merstham	Metropolitan Police	Needham Market	Staines Town	Tonbridge Angels	VCD Athletic	Wingate & Finchley
Billericay Town		2-0	1-1	0-0	0-3	4-1	3-1	3-0	2-3	1-1	0-1	2-1	3-1	0-0	2-0	4-1	1-1	1-1	6-0	1-1	2-3	1-1	1-1	4-0
Bognor Regis Town	3-1		3-1	2-1	5-0	2-3	2-2	1-1	4-1	3-0	1-0	1-0	4-0	0-0	5-0	3-0	4-0	4-3	2-1	2-1	3-0	0-5	2-0	6-0
Brentwood Town	1-1	0-1		1-1	3-3	1-2	1-3	1-2	1-1	1-2	0-3	2-1	4-1	0-0	4-1	0-2	0-1	1-2	2-2	1-0	7-0	0-1	2-0	0-1
Burgess Hill Town	1-1	0-4	1-1		3-2	3-2	0-2	1-0	3-1	1-2	1-2	0-5	0-1	1-3	1-2	1-1	2-1	5-1	4-2	2-2	0-2	0-0		0-1
Canvey Island	0-2	1-1	1-0	3-3		1-2	2-4	2-0	1-0	0-3	0-4	1-0	3-2	2-1	3-1	1-1	5-2	0-2	0-3	1-2	2-3	1-1	2-1	2-1
Dulwich Hamlet	1-0	2-0	4-0	1-1	3-0		2-2	2-0	2-2	1-1	3-3	4-0	4-2	5-1	1-0	1-1	2-1	4-0	1-2	0-1	1-2	2-1	5-2	2-1
East Thurrock United	1-1	0-0	4-0	1-1	4-0	2-2		1-0	4-1	3-0	2-1	2-0	2-4	2-2	4-4	4-0	4-1	1-4	2-1	1-2	0-0	3-0	4-1	1-1
Enfield Town	2-2	2-1	2-1	1-0	2-1	2-2	1-1		4-1	2-0	2-3	3-0	2-0	4-0	4-0	0-2	2-1	2-2	2-0	3-0	2-1	0-1	3-0	2-0
Farnborough	0-2	2-1	3-0	1-0	2-6	1-4	0-3	0-0		5-0	0-3	2-1	1-0	3-2	1-3	5-1	0-3	0-1	1-1	2-3	1-2	3-0	2-1	
Grays Athletic	2-0	0-2	4-0	1-2	1-0	1-2	0-0	1-0	3-1		0-3	3-2	1-1	1-3	0-2	4-0	1-3	3-3	0-2	1-1	1-1	0-1	0-0	
Hampton & Richmond Borough	2-1	2-1	5-1	1-1	5-0	2-1	2-1	0-0	3-1	3-1		2-2	5-0	3-1	2-0	4-3	0-4	2-1	1-0	5-0	3-2	2-2	4-0	1-2
Harrow Borough	2-1	1-2	1-0	0-1	1-2	1-0	2-5	1-2	3-1	3-0	1-1		5-5	1-3	2-2	0-0	4-1	0-2	0-2	1-0	1-1	1-1	1-2	1-0
Hendon	1-1	1-1	1-0	2-2	1-1	1-2	1-0	3-0	2-2	1-0	0-1			1-1	2-3	2-4	2-0	2-2	0-2	0-2	0-0	0-3	3-1	4-3
Kingstonian	2-2	2-1	4-0	1-0	1-1	0-3	1-4	1-0	1-2	2-1	4-1	5-2	1-0		0-3	1-0	2-2	3-1	7-0	1-0	0-3	2-1	3-0	2-1
Leatherhead	4-1	0-3	1-0	3-2	4-4	1-0	2-1	0-3	0-1	3-0	2-2	1-2	2-5	0-0		3-2	3-0	0-2	1-3	2-2	3-0	0-2	2-0	0-0
Leiston	1-1	0-2	2-0	1-1	1-1	1-1	0-3	2-0	4-2	1-2	3-1	2-0	2-0	2-1	3-1		3-1	1-1	3-0	3-1	1-2	3-0	0-1	
Lewes	2-3	0-2	1-5	1-2	3-1	3-1	1-1	0-2	1-0	1-1	1-1	2-2	1-2	3-4	1-1			1-0	2-0	0-2	1-1	2-2	1-2	0-0
Merstham	0-2	3-2	1-3	1-2	1-0	0-2	2-2	0-4	1-1	2-2	1-6	0-1	0-1	3-1	1-2	0-2	2-2		1-0	2-0	5-1	2-2	6-1	0-2
Metropolitan Police	1-0	1-0	0-0	1-1	0-1	1-3	0-3	2-2	1-2	2-4	0-3	3-2	3-0	2-1	1-0	0-3	0-0	2-3		1-0	0-0	0-3	1-1	1-3
Needham Market	1-3	0-1	4-0	1-2	2-3	2-1	1-4	3-2	0-2	0-0	1-1	2-4	0-3	0-0	2-2	1-0	1-0	1-1	0-1		0-1	2-1	0-3	1-3
Staines Town	0-1	0-1	0-1	2-2	2-2	1-3	3-2	0-1	2-0	0-4	1-2	1-3	0-2	1-2	3-0	2-0	3-1	0-2				1-1	1-0	1-2
Tonbridge Angels	2-2	1-3	4-0	2-3	2-0	1-1	1-2	3-1	2-0	2-3	1-0	3-3	3-1	1-1	4-0	1-0	3-2	0-1	3-3	2-0			7-0	4-3
VCD Athletic	2-3	1-1	0-2	2-2	0-1	3-2	3-2	2-1	4-2	1-1	1-2	2-3	2-3	0-3	0-1	0-0	1-3	3-3	1-1	0-3	0-3			2-1
Wingate & Finchley	0-1	1-3	2-1	5-1	1-2	1-1	1-3	1-2	4-3	3-2	1-3	1-1	2-1	1-1	1-0	1-1	1-3	1-3	6-0	0-0	0-1	2-0		

Ryman League Premier Division

Season 2015/2016

Team	P	W	D	L	F	A	Pts
Hampton & Richmond Borough	46	28	11	7	105	52	95
Bognor Regis Town	46	29	7	10	95	42	94
East Thurrock United	46	26	13	7	107	53	91
Tonbridge Angels	46	24	13	9	90	49	85
Dulwich Hamlet	46	23	12	11	93	58	81
Enfield Town	46	24	8	14	74	47	80
Kingstonian	46	21	10	15	78	64	73
Leiston	46	20	12	14	72	57	72
Billericay Town	46	18	17	11	76	53	71
Merstham	46	18	8	20	74	80	62
Leatherhead	46	18	8	20	67	81	62
Metropolitan Police	46	17	10	19	60	79	61
Wingate & Finchley	46	17	9	20	66	70	60
Canvey Island	46	17	9	20	69	89	60
Grays Athletic	46	15	12	19	63	74	57
Staines Town	46	15	10	21	53	74	55
Harrow Borough	46	15	9	22	66	80	54
Farnborough	46	16	5	25	65	88	53
Hendon	46	13	13	20	68	85	52
Needham Market	46	13	12	21	51	76	51
Burgess Hill Town	46	12	14	20	57	73	50
Brentwood Town	46	10	10	26	51	80	40
Lewes	46	6	16	24	48	87	34
VCD Athletic	46	8	10	28	46	103	34

Farnborough were demoted at the end of the season after financial irregularities were discovered.

Promotion Play-offs

Bognor Regis Town 0   Dulwich Hamlet 1
East Thurrock United 2   Tonbridge Angels 0

East Thurrock United 3   Dulwich Hamlet 0

Promoted: Hampton & Richmond Borough and Dulwich Hamlet

Relegated: Farnborough, Brentwood Town, Lewes and VCD Athletic

F.A. Trophy 2015/2016

Qualifying 1	Marine	1	Sheffield	0
Qualifying 1	Witton Albion	1	Radcliffe Borough	2
Qualifying 1	Buxton	2	Frickley Athletic	1
Qualifying 1	Blyth Spartans	4	Kendal Town	0
Qualifying 1	Shaw Lane Aquaforce	4	Farsley Celtic	3
Qualifying 1	Workington	0	Whitby Town	3
Qualifying 1	Northwich Victoria	1	Stocksbridge Park Steels	2
Qualifying 1	Nantwich Town	2	Salford City	1
Qualifying 1	Spennymoor Town	6	Goole	3
Qualifying 1	Ashton United	2	Ramsbottom United	2
Qualifying 1	Skelmersdale United	3	Hyde United	3
Qualifying 1	Warrington Town	2	Brighouse Town	0
Qualifying 1	Burscough	1	Colwyn Bay	0
Qualifying 1	Darlington 1883	3	Mossley	2
Qualifying 1	Leamington	6	Barwell	1
Qualifying 1	Cambridge City	0	Ilkeston	1
Qualifying 1	Sutton Coldfield Town	2	Coalville Town	0
Qualifying 1	Evesham United	1	Redditch United	0
Qualifying 1	Carlton Town	2	Stamford	1
Qualifying 1	Belper Town	1	King's Lynn Town	1
Qualifying 1	Histon	0	Stratford Town	0
Qualifying 1	Basford United	3	Grantham Town	1
Qualifying 1	St Ives Town	0	Kettering Town	1
Qualifying 1	Rushall Olympic	1	Mickleover Sports	0
Qualifying 1	Stafford Rangers	1	Lincoln United	1
Qualifying 1	Halesowen Town	1	Stourbridge	2
Qualifying 1	Newcastle Town	2	Kidsgrove Athletic	2
Qualifying 1	Matlock Town	2	Gresley	0
Qualifying 1	St Neots Town	2	Bedworth United	0
Qualifying 1	Northwood	1	Bedford Town	3
Qualifying 1	East Thurrock United	4	South Park	0
Qualifying 1	Corinthian Casuals	4	Redbridge	1
Qualifying 1	Chipstead	1	Hastings United	2
Qualifying 1	Leatherhead	1	Kingstonian	5
Qualifying 1	Enfield Town	4	Leighton Town	0
Qualifying 1	Aylesbury	1	Brentwood Town	1
Qualifying 1	Phoenix Sports	1	Tonbridge Angels	1
Qualifying 1	Herne Bay	1	Walton Casuals	1
Qualifying 1	AFC Hornchurch	2	Metropolitan Police	3
Qualifying 1	Thurrock	3	Chatham Town	0
Qualifying 1	VCD Athletic	2	Staines Town	1
Qualifying 1	Chalfont St Peter	1	Waltham Abbey	3
Qualifying 1	Cheshunt	2	Heybridge Swifts	0
Qualifying 1	Billericay Town	0	Chesham United	2
Qualifying 1	Thamesmead Town	1	Ramsgate	0
Qualifying 1	Bognor Regis Town	3	East Grinstead Town	0
Qualifying 1	Tilbury	2	Tooting & Mitcham United	1
Qualifying 1	Dunstable Town	1	Haringey Borough	3
Qualifying 1	Hitchin Town	3	Burgess Hill Town	2
Qualifying 1	Lewes	0	Hampton & Richmond Borough	0
Qualifying 1	Grays Athletic	2	Biggleswade Town	1
Qualifying 1	Romford	0	Slough Town	4
Qualifying 1	Wingate & Finchley	0	Royston Town	2
Qualifying 1	Harrow Borough	0	Dulwich Hamlet	3
Qualifying 1	Hendon	0	AFC Sudbury	1

Qualifying 1	Worthing	1	Leiston	3	
Qualifying 1	Merstham	0	Harlow Town	0	
Qualifying 1	Bury Town	2	Kings Langley	0	
Qualifying 1	Needham Market	0	Canvey Island	2	
Qualifying 1	Paulton Rovers	2	Swindon Supermarine	3	
Qualifying 1	Molesey	1	Didcot Town	0	
Qualifying 1	Taunton Town	1	Dorking Wanderers	1	
Qualifying 1	Hungerford Town	0	Banbury United	0	
Qualifying 1	Cirencester Town	2	North Leigh	1	
Qualifying 1	Dorchester Town	2	Chippenham Town	1	
Qualifying 1	Mangotsfield United	6	Bashley	1	
Qualifying 1	Egham Town	1	Frome Town	2	
Qualifying 1	Merthyr Town	1	Poole Town	0	
Qualifying 1	Peacehaven & Telscombe	0	Tiverton Town	3	
Qualifying 1	Winchester City	1	Weymouth	2	
Qualifying 1	Bideford	1	Farnborough	1	
Qualifying 1	Marlow	3	Larkhall Athletic	0	
Replay	Banbury United	0	Hungerford Town	3	
Replay	Brentwood Town	2	Aylesbury	0	
Replay	Dorking Wanderers	1	Taunton Town	3	
Replay	Farnborough	2	Bideford	2	(aet)
	Bideford won 5-4 on penalties				
Replay	Hampton & Richmond Borough	2	Lewes	1	
Replay	Harlow Town	6	Merstham	2	
Replay	Hyde United	0	Skelmersdale United	1	
Replay	Kidsgrove Athletic	3	Newcastle Town	0	
Replay	King's Lynn Town	5	Belper Town	1	
Replay	Lincoln United	1	Stafford Rangers	1	(aet)
	Lincoln United won 5-4 on penalties				
Replay	Ramsbottom United	2	Ashton United	2	(aet)
	Ashton United won 10-9 on penalties				
Replay	Stratford Town	4	Histon	1	
Replay	Tonbridge Angels	2	Phoenix Sports	0	
Replay	Walton Casuals	2	Herne Bay	3	
Qualifying 2	Blyth Spartans	1	Whitby Town	0	
Qualifying 2	Ashton United	2	Stratford Town	1	
Qualifying 2	Evesham United	1	Spennymoor Town	2	
Qualifying 2	Buxton	5	Radcliffe Borough	1	
Qualifying 2	Skelmersdale United	4	Lincoln United	2	
Qualifying 2	Sutton Coldfield Town	1	Darlington 1883	0	
Qualifying 2	Nantwich Town	5	King's Lynn Town	1	
Qualifying 2	Shaw Lane Aquaforce	1	Matlock Town	2	
Qualifying 2	Leamington	0	Rushall Olympic	0	
Qualifying 2	Warrington Town	3	Basford United	0	
Qualifying 2	Marine	2	Kidsgrove Athletic	2	
Qualifying 2	Ilkeston	1	Stocksbridge Park Steels	1	
Qualifying 2	Kettering Town	0	Burscough	3	
Qualifying 2	Stourbridge	2	Carlton Town	0	
Qualifying 2	Bideford	3	Brentwood Town	2	
Qualifying 2	St Neots Town	1	Hungerford Town	2	
Qualifying 2	Haringey Borough	1	Hitchin Town	1	
Qualifying 2	Thurrock	3	Cheshunt	1	
Qualifying 2	Tonbridge Angels	1	Cirencester Town	2	
Qualifying 2	Enfield Town	0	Thamesmead Town	2	
Qualifying 2	Tilbury	4	Royston Town	2	
Qualifying 2	Leiston	1	Corinthian Casuals	2	
Qualifying 2	Bedford Town	1	Weymouth	4	

Round	Home	Score	Away	Score	
Qualifying 2	Swindon Supermarine	2	Chesham United	3	
Qualifying 2	Taunton Town	1	Bognor Regis Town	4	
Qualifying 2	Molesey	4	Harlow Town	3	
Qualifying 2	East Thurrock United	5	Tiverton Town	0	
Qualifying 2	Waltham Abbey	0	Grays Athletic	2	
Qualifying 2	Dulwich Hamlet	2	VCD Athletic	0	
Qualifying 2	Frome Town	2	Slough Town	1	
Qualifying 2	Hampton & Richmond Borough	3	AFC Sudbury	1	
Qualifying 2	Dorchester Town	2	Kingstonian	2	
Qualifying 2	Marlow	1	Mangotsfield United	0	
Qualifying 2	Canvey Island	0	Metropolitan Police	2	
Qualifying 2	Hastings United	1	Merthyr Town	2	
Qualifying 2	Bury Town	1	Herne Bay	1	
Replay	Herne Bay	1	Bury Town	1	(aet)
	Bury Town won 4-3 on penalties				
Replay	Hitchin Town	3	Haringey Borough	0	
Replay	Kidsgrove Athletic	0	Marine	1	
Replay	Kingstonian	2	Dorchester Town	1	
Replay	Rushall Olympic	2	Leamington	3	(aet)
Replay	Stocksbridge Park Steels	3	Ilkeston	2	
Qualifying 3	FC United of Manchester	1	AFC Telford United	2	
Qualifying 3	Solihull Moors	1	Boston United	0	
Qualifying 3	Leamington	4	Hednesford Town	2	
Qualifying 3	Stourbridge	4	Spennymoor Town	2	
Qualifying 3	Harrogate Town	0	Curzon Ashton	1	
Qualifying 3	Marine	1	Burscough	2	
Qualifying 3	Corby Town	2	Tamworth	6	
Qualifying 3	Gainsborough Trinity	0	Ashton United	0	
Qualifying 3	Brackley Town	0	Worcester City	2	
Qualifying 3	Chorley	0	Skelmersdale United	0	
Qualifying 3	Warrington Town	0	AFC Fylde	2	
Qualifying 3	Buxton	1	Bradford (Park Avenue)	2	
Qualifying 3	Matlock Town	4	Blyth Spartans	2	
Qualifying 3	Nuneaton Town	2	Alfreton Town	0	
Qualifying 3	Sutton Coldfield Town	1	Stalybridge Celtic	0	
Qualifying 3	North Ferriby United	1	Stocksbridge Park Steels	2	
Qualifying 3	Stockport County	0	Nantwich Town	2	
Qualifying 3	Merthyr Town	1	East Thurrock United	1	
Qualifying 3	Hampton & Richmond Borough	0	Maidstone United	1	
Qualifying 3	Ebbsfleet United	4	Molesey	1	
Qualifying 3	Maidenhead United	4	Bideford	0	
Qualifying 3	Cirencester Town	2	Gosport Borough	1	
Qualifying 3	Hungerford Town	3	Thamesmead Town	0	
Qualifying 3	Tilbury	3	Bishopʹs Stortford	0	
Qualifying 3	Weston Super Mare	4	Hitchin Town	0	
Qualifying 3	Oxford City	6	Marlow	3	
Qualifying 3	Chelmsford City	1	Gloucester City	1	
Qualifying 3	Lowestoft Town	4	St Albans City	0	
Qualifying 3	Metropolitan Police	0	Wealdstone	2	
Qualifying 3	Hemel Hempstead Town	1	Weymouth	0	
Qualifying 3	Dartford	1	Whitehawk	2	
Qualifying 3	Sutton United	0	Concord Rangers	2	
Qualifying 3	Frome Town	1	Chesham United	1	
Qualifying 3	Bury Town	4	Thurrock	2	
Qualifying 3	Dulwich Hamlet	2	Margate	1	
Qualifying 3	Grays Athletic	0	Corinthian Casuals	0	

Qualifying 3	Bognor Regis Town	1	Bath City	0	
Qualifying 3	Havant & Waterlooville	2	Basingstoke Town	1	
Qualifying 3	Hayes & Yeading United	2	Eastbourne Borough	2	
Qualifying 3	Kingstonian	0	Truro City	3	
Replay	Ashton United	3	Gainsborough Trinity	1	
Replay	Chesham United	2	Frome Town	1	
Replay	Corinthian Casuals	1	Grays Athletic	0	
Replay	Eastbourne Borough	4	Hayes & Yeading United	0	
Replay	East Thurrock United	3	Merthyr Town	1	
Replay	Gloucester City	0	Chelmsford City	1	
Replay	Skelmersdale United	5	Chorley	2	
Round 1	FC Halifax Town	5	Tamworth	0	
Round 1	Grimsby Town	1	Solihull Moors	1	
Round 1	Sutton Coldfield Town	0	Barrow	2	
Round 1	Burscough	2	Guiseley	2	
Round 1	Macclesfield Town	4	Ashton United	0	
Round 1	Nantwich Town	2	Matlock Town	0	
Round 1	Southport	0	Worcester City	0	
Round 1	Curzon Ashton	3	Nuneaton Town	1	
Round 1	Altrincham	1	Leamington	1	
Round 1	AFC Telford United	0	Chester	2	
Round 1	Stourbridge	2	Kidderminster Harriers	1	
Round 1	Gateshead	4	Stocksbridge Park Steels	1	
Round 1	AFC Fylde	4	Skelmersdale United	4	
Round 1	Bradford (Park Avenue)	2	Lincoln City	1	
Round 1	Tranmere Rovers	2	Wrexham	4	
Round 1	Eastbourne Borough	7	Hemel Hempstead Town	4	
Round 1	Tilbury	3	Welling United	4	
Round 1	Truro City	2	Cirencester Town	2	
Round 1	Torquay United	0	Chesham United	0	
Round 1	Whitehawk	1	Dover Athletic	3	
Round 1	Corinthian Casuals	1	Hungerford Town	2	
Round 1	Boreham Wood	1	Woking	2	
Round 1	Sutton United	3	Lowestoft Town	1	
Round 1	Maidstone United	0	Bognor Regis Town	1	
Round 1	Cheltenham Town	3	Chelmsford City	1	
Round 1	East Thurrock United	1	Maidenhead United	4	
Round 1	Oxford City	3	Ebbsfleet United	1	
Round 1	Aldershot Town	0	Eastleigh	1	
Round 1	Weston Super Mare	3	Wealdstone	2	
Round 1	Havant & Waterlooville	2	Forest Green Rovers	0	
Round 1	Bury Town	1	Dulwich Hamlet	2	
Round 1	Braintree Town	1	Bromley	0	
Replay	Chesham United	0	Torquay United	2	
Replay	Cirencester Town	0	Truro City	1	
Replay	Guiseley	3	Burscough	2	
Replay	Leamington	1	Altrincham	2	(aet)
Replay	Skelmersdale United	0	AFC Fylde	4	
Replay	Solihull Moors	2	Grimsby Town	3	
Replay	Worcester City	2	Southport	3	
Round 2	Dulwich Hamlet	1	Guiseley	2	
Round 2	Dover Athletic	2	Southport	1	
Round 2	Havant & Waterlooville	2	Welling United	1	
Round 2	Truro City	2	Macclesfield Town	2	
Round 2	Braintree Town	0	Stourbridge	1	
Round 2	Chester	4	Hungerford Town	0	

Round 2	Eastbourne Borough	1	AFC Fylde	4	
Round 2	Sutton United	1	Curzon Ashton	0	
Round 2	Torquay United	1	Wrexham	0	
Round 2	Grimsby Town	3	Weston Super Mare	1	
Round 2	FC Halifax Town	1	Barrow	0	
Round 2	Eastleigh	1	Gateshead	2	
Round 2	Bognor Regis Town	2	Altrincham	1	
Round 2	Bradford (Park Avenue)	1	Nantwich Town	1	
Round 2	Woking	6	Maidenhead United	1	
Round 2	Oxford City	2	Cheltenham Town	2	
Replay	Cheltenham Town	0	Oxford City	3	
Replay	Macclesfield Town	2	Truro City	0	
Replay	Nantwich Town	5	Bradford (Park Avenue)	0	
Round 3	Torquay United	3	Macclesfield Town	3	
Round 3	Grimsby Town	3	Havant & Waterlooville	0	
Round 3	Gateshead	1	AFC Fylde	0	
Round 3	FC Halifax Town	1	Chester	0	
Round 3	Woking	1	Oxford City	0	
Round 3	Dover Athletic	2	Guiseley	2	
Round 3	Sutton United	0	Bognor Regis Town	0	
Round 3	Nantwich Town	1	Stourbridge	0	
Replay	Bognor Regis Town	2	Sutton United	1	
Replay	Guiseley	0	Dover Athletic	3	
Replay	Macclesfield Town	0	Torquay United	1	
Round 4	Nantwich Town	2	Dover Athletic	1	
Round 4	FC Halifax Town	0	Gateshead	0	
Round 4	Grimsby Town	2	Woking	0	
Round 4	Bognor Regis Town	1	Torquay United	0	
Replay	Gateshead	3	FC Halifax Town	3	(aet)
	FC Halifax Town won 5-4 on penalties				

Semi-finals

1st leg	Nantwich Town	2	FC Halifax Town	4
2nd leg	FC Halifax Town	2	Nantwich Town	2
	FC Halifax Town won 6-4 on aggregate			
1st leg	Bognor Regis Town	0	Grimsby Town	1
2nd leg	Grimsby Town	2	Bognor Regis Town	1
	Grimsby Town won 3-1 on aggregate			
FINAL	FC Halifax Town	1	Grimsby Town	0

F.A. Vase 2015/2016

Round	Home		Away		
Round 1	West Didsbury & Chorlton	4	Morpeth Town	5	
Round 1	Handsworth Parramore	5	Shildon	4	(aet)
Round 1	Guisborough Town	8	Armthorpe Welfare	0	
Round 1	Atherton Collieries	2	Newcastle Benfield	0	
Round 1	Stokesley	1	Maltby Main	4	(aet)
Round 1	Silsden	2	Sunderland RCA	4	
Round 1	Rochdale Town	2	1874 Northwich	4	
Round 1	Runcorn Linnets	2	Winsford United	1	
Round 1	Team Northumbria	4	Darlington RA	0	
Round 1	Congleton Town	1	Marske United	5	
Round 1	Athersley Recreation	1	Colne	5	
Round 1	Durham City	0	Seaham Red Star	1	
Round 1	Dronfield Town	2	Ashington	3	(aet)
Round 1	Chester-Le-Street Town	0	Newton Aycliffe	4	
Round 1	Selby Town	1	Hallam	2	
Round 1	Runcorn Town	2	Abbey Hey	0	
Round 1	Hemsworth MW	3	West Auckland Town	2	
Round 1	Northwich Manchester Villa	1	Whitley Bay	1	(aet)
Round 1	Garforth Town	1	Hebburn Town	0	
Round 1	Bishop Auckland	1	South Shields	2	
Round 1	Highgate United	3	Radcliffe Olympic	1	
Round 1	Loughborough University	0	Uttoxeter Town	0	(aet)
Round 1	Dunkirk	2	Bromsgrove Sporting	1	
Round 1	Pinxton	1	Cradley Town	0	
Round 1	Rocester	0	Hereford	2	
Round 1	Coventry Sphinx	1	Black Country Rangers	1	(aet)
Round 1	Alsager Town	2	Borrowash Victoria	2	(aet)
	Alsager Town won 5-4 on penalties				
Round 1	Wisbech Town	0	Alvechurch	4	
Round 1	Cleethorpes Town	2	Westfields	1	
Round 1	Blackstones	2	Haughmond	3	(aet)
Round 1	Shirebrook Town	2	Sporting Khalsa	0	
Round 1	Radford	1	AFC Bridgnorth	3	
Round 1	St Andrews	3	Blidworth Welfare	3	(aet)
Round 1	Coleshill Town	3	Hucknall Town	0	
Round 1	AFC Wulfrunians	4	Harrowby United	2	(aet)
Round 1	Racing Club Warwick	3	Ellesmere Rangers	2	
Round 1	Nuneaton Griff	1	Anstey Nomads	0	
Round 1	Quorn	1	Clipstone Welfare	0	
Round 1	Boldmere St Michaels	0	Coventry United	2	
Round 1	Long Eaton United	2	Hinckley	1	(aet)
Round 1	Stotfold	5	Newmarket Town	0	
Round 1	Cricklewood Wanderers	1	Welwyn Garden City	0	
Round 1	Diss Town	2	Basildon United	3	
Round 1	Barking	4	Tring Athletic	1	
Round 1	Bowers & Pitsea	3	Hanworth Villa	2	
Round 1	Hadley	2	FC Romania	3	
Round 1	Northampton Sileby Rangers	5	Wembley	4	
Round 1	Brantham Athletic	0	Kirkley & Pakefield	4	
Round 1	Gorleston	6	London Tigers	3	(aet)
Round 1	Ipswich Wanderers	2	Hoddesdon Town	1	
Round 1	Berkhamsted	5	Northampton Spencer	1	
Round 1	London Colney	2	Great Yarmouth Town	1	
Round 1	AFC Dunstable	2	FC Clacton	0	(aet)
Round 1	Raunds Town	0	Sleaford Town	1	

Round 1	Hertford Town	4	Eynesbury Rovers	3	
Round 1	Godmanchester Rovers	1	Mildenhall Town	1	(aet)
Round 1	Ilford	0	AFC Kempston Rovers	1	
Round 1	Sporting Bengal United	6	Southall	2	
Round 1	Swaffham Town	1	FC Broxbourne Borough	2	
Round 1	Edgware Town	5	Whitton United	2	
Round 1	Biggleswade United	2	Cogenhoe United	0	
Round 1	Harefield United	0	Greenhouse Sports	3	
Round 1	Eastbourne Town	3	Farnham Town	2	(aet)
Round 1	Hartley Wintney	3	Wokingham & Emmbrook	1	
Round 1	Worthing United	0	Sutton Common Rovers	1	
Round 1	Knaphill	5	Cray Valley Paper Mills	4	(aet)
Round 1	Deal Town	4	Oxford City Nomads	2	
Round 1	Littlehampton Town	1	Tadley Calleva	2	
Round 1	Andover Town	1	Newhaven	2	
Round 1	Cove	0	Canterbury City	5	
Round 1	Corinthian	2	Pagham	3	
Round 1	AFC Croydon Athletic	2	Beckenham Town	2	(aet)
Round 1	Loxwood	3	Highmoor Ibis	1	
Round 1	Haywards Heath Town	1	Alton Town	0	
Round 1	Kidlington	2	Ashford Town (Middx)	2	(aet)
Round 1	Bedfont Sports	1	Carterton	4	
Round 1	Lancing	1	Camberley Town	2	
Round 1	Hailsham Town	1	Gravesham Borough	0	
Round 1	Windsor	3	Croydon	2	
Round 1	Steyning Town	1	Horsham	0	(aet)
Round 1	Thame United	4	Bridon Ropes	3	
Round 1	Meridian VP	1	Lordswood	4	
Round 1	Bristol Manor Farm	3	Bridport	0	
Round 1	Plymouth Parkway	6	Blackfield & Langley	0	
Round 1	Moneyfields	1	Corsham Town	0	
Round 1	Witheridge	0	Hallen	1	
Round 1	Horndean	1	Barnstaple Town	3	
Round 1	Lymington Town	2	Wells City	0	
Round 1	Calne Town	2	Salisbury	6	
Round 1	Whitchurch United	2	Welton Rovers	2	(aet)
Round 1	Team Solent	2	Cadbury Heath	3	
Round 1	Odd Down	2	Camelford	1	
Round 1	Portishead Town	1	Newport (IW)	3	
Round 1	AFC Portchester	1	Abbey Rangers	2	
Round 1	Gillingham Town	0	Hengrove Athletic	0	(aet)
	Hengrove Athletic won 5-4 on penalties				
Round 1	New Milton Town	0	Buckland Athletic	5	
Round 1	Sholing	3	Laverstock & Ford	1	
Round 1	Bishop Sutton	0	Torpoint Athletic	3	
Round 1	Fairford Town	0	Brimscombe & Thrupp	1	
Replay	Ashford Town (Middx)	1	Kidlington	3	
Replay	Beckenham Town	6	AFC Croydon Athletic	3	(aet)
Replay	Black Country Rangers	4	Coventry Sphinx	6	(aet)
Replay	Blidworth Welfare	0	St Andrews	2	(aet)
Replay	Mildenhall Town	2	Godmanchester Rovers	1	
Replay	Uttoxeter Town	3	Loughborough University	2	
Replay	Welton Rovers	4	Whitchurch United	0	
Replay	Whitley Bay	3	Northwich Manchester Villa	1	

Round 2	Runcorn Town	3	Garforth Town	0	
Round 2	North Shields	3	Ashington	0	
Round 2	Atherton Collieries	3	Chadderton	0	
Round 2	Morpeth Town	w/o	1874 Northwich		
	The original match was postponed and 1874 Northwich conceded the tie after being unable to raise a team for the date of the replay.				
Round 2	Colne	3	Newton Aycliffe	5	(aet)
Round 2	Seaham Red Star	3	Maltby Main	1	
Round 2	Handsworth Parramore	3	Hallam	2	
Round 2	Hemsworth MW	1	Sunderland RCA	5	
Round 2	Consett	0	South Shields	1	(aet)
Round 2	Whitley Bay	1	Dunston UTS	2	
Round 2	Marske United	6	Runcorn Linnets	2	
Round 2	Tadcaster Albion	4	Worksop Town	1	
Round 2	Guisborough Town	1	Team Northumbria	2	(aet)
Round 2	AFC Mansfield	1	Alsager Town	1	(aet)
Round 2	Walsall Wood	4	Holbeach United	1	
Round 2	AFC Bridgnorth	1	Alvechurch	2	
Round 2	Coventry Sphinx	2	Brocton	3	
Round 2	Coventry United	1	Uttoxeter Town	2	
Round 2	Coleshill Town	4	Dunkirk	2	
Round 2	Hereford	4	Haughmond	1	
Round 2	Long Eaton United	2	Pinxton	3	
Round 2	Heanor Town	1	Leicester Nirvana	3	
Round 2	Cleethorpes Town	2	Racing Club Warwick	0	
Round 2	Quorn	1	AFC Wulfunians	2	
Round 2	Nuneaton Griff	1	Highgate United	1	(aet)
Round 2	St Andrews	4	Shirebrook Town	0	
Round 2	Stotfold	1	AFC Dunstable	3	
Round 2	Bowers & Pitsea	3	Flackwell Heath	2	
Round 2	Yaxley	3	London Colney	2	
Round 2	Sporting Bengal United	1	Sleaford Town	3	(aet)
Round 2	Gorleston	3	FC Romania	4	(aet)
Round 2	Ipswich Wanderers	1	Cricklewood Wanderers	0	
Round 2	FC Broxbourne Borough	2	Greenhouse Sports	1	(aet)
Round 2	Norwich United	0	Hullbridge Sports	1	(aet)
Round 2	Hertford Town	3	Barking	2	
Round 2	Biggleswade United	1	Saffron Walden Town	3	
Round 2	Kirkley & Pakefield	1	Edgware Town	2	
Round 2	Basildon United	7	Northampton Sileby Rangers	1	
Round 2	Stanway Rovers	2	Mildenhall Town	1	
Round 2	Berkhamsted	3	AFC Kempston Rovers	1	
Round 2	Sutton Common Rovers	3	Beckenham Town	2	
Round 2	Knaphill	3	Tunbridge Wells	0	
Round 2	Newhaven	1	Camberley Town	2	
Round 2	Ashford United	2	Steyning Town	1	
Round 2	Eastbourne Town	5	Greenwich Borough	4	
Round 2	Pagham	0	Thame United	3	
Round 2	Lordswood	4	Carterton	1	
Round 2	Hailsham Town	1	Ascot United	4	
Round 2	Canterbury City	3	Erith & Belvedere	2	
Round 2	Tadley Calleva	4	Haywards Heath Town	0	
Round 2	Kidlington	7	Deal Town	0	
Round 2	Colliers Wood United	2	Loxwood	0	
Round 2	Hartley Wintney	3	Windsor	1	
Round 2	Hallen	0	Moneyfields	1	

Round 2	Highworth Town	2	Odd Down	1	
Round 2	Salisbury	4	AFC St Austell	0	
Round 2	Bradford Town	6	Cadbury Heath	3	
Round 2	Buckland Athletic	2	Sholing	1	(aet)
Round 2	Welton Rovers	1	Plymouth Parkway	0	
Round 2	Newport (IW)	3	Abbey Rangers	1	
Round 2	Bodmin Town	3	Melksham Town	1	
Round 2	Bristol Manor Farm	2	Lymington Town	1	
Round 2	Hengrove Athletic	2	Barnstaple Town	1	
Round 2	Brimscombe & Thrupp	3	Torpoint Athletic	2	
Replay	Alsager Town	3	AFC Mansfield	1	
Replay	Highgate United	2	Nuneaton Griff	4	
Round 3	Team Northumbria	1	Marske United	2	
Round 3	Sunderland RCA	4	Tadcaster Albion	0	
Round 3	Newton Aycliffe	1	Atherton Collieries	0	
Round 3	South Shields	3	Morpeth Town	3	(aet)
	Morpeth Town won 10-9 on penalties				
Round 3	North Shields	1	Runcorn Town	1	(aet)
Round 3	Dunston UTS	1	Seaham Red Star	0	
Round 3	Alsager Town	0	AFC Wulfunians	2	
Round 3	St Andrews	1	Leicester Nirvana	5	
Round 3	Handsworth Parramore	1	Cleethorpes Town	2	
Round 3	Pinxton	3	Nuneaton Griff	4	
Round 3	Walsall Wood	0	Alvechurch	3	
Round 3	Uttoxeter Town	3	Coleshill Town	4	
Round 3	Hereford	2	Brocton	0	
Round 3	Saffron Walden Town	2	Berkhamsted	3	
Round 3	FC Broxbourne Borough	1	Bowers & Pitsea	3	
Round 3	Hullbridge Sports	2	Stanway Rovers	0	
Round 3	AFC Dunstable	4	Basildon United	0	
Round 3	Edgware Town	0	Ipswich Wanderers	3	
Round 3	Yaxley	3	Sleaford Town	4	(aet)
Round 3	Hertford Town	0	FC Romania	2	
Round 3	Colliers Wood United	1	Hartley Wintney	3	
Round 3	Thame United	1	Kidlington	2	
Round 3	Ascot United	0	Camberley Town	0	(aet)
Round 3	Lordswood	1	Ashford United	5	
Round 3	Eastbourne Town	2	Sutton Common Rovers	3	
Round 3	Tadley Calleva	2	Newport (IW)	2	(aet)
Round 3	Canterbury City	1	Knaphill	3	
Round 3	Moneyfields	0	Brimscombe & Thrupp	0	(aet)
Round 3	Buckland Athletic	1	Bradford Town	2	
Round 3	Highworth Town	1	Salisbury	5	
Round 3	Welton Rovers	0	Bodmin Town	2	
Round 3	Bristol Manor Farm	7	Hengrove Athletic	1	
Replay	Brimscombe & Thrupp	0	Moneyfields	2	
Replay	Camberley Town	4	Ascot United	1	
Replay	Newport (IW)	4	Tadley Calleva	2	(aet)
Replay	Runcorn Town	0	North Shields	1	
Round 4	Cleethorpes Town	2	Alvechurch	1	
Round 4	Hereford	6	Leicester Nirvana	0	
Round 4	North Shields	0	Morpeth Town	2	
Round 4	Coleshill Town	1	Dunston UTS	3	(aet)
Round 4	AFC Wulfrunians	2	Nuneaton Griff	3	

Round 4	Sunderland RCA	3	Sleaford Town	2	
Round 4	Newton Aycliffe	2	Marske United	0	
Round 4	Bowers & Pitsea	3	Sutton Common Rovers	0	
Round 4	Kidlington	3	Knaphill	2	
Round 4	Newport (IW)	1	Ashford United	2	(aet)
Round 4	Moneyfields	0	Bristol Manor Farm	2	
Round 4	FC Romania	1	Camberley Town	2	
Round 4	AFC Dunstable	0	Salisbury	3	
Round 4	Berkhamsted	4	Hullbridge Sports	2	
Round 4	Hartley & Wintney	3	Bradford Town	1	
Round 4	Bodmin Town	1	Ipswich Wanderers	3	
Round 5	Ipswich Wanderers	1	Bowers & Pitsea	1	(aet)
Round 5	Sunderland RCA	2	Bristol Manor Farm	3	
Round 5	Camberley Town	5	Newton Aycliffe	0	
Round 5	Berkhamsted	1	Morpeth Town	2	
Round 5	Cleethorpes Town	1	Kidlington	2	
Round 5	Nuneaton Griff	0	Salisbury	3	
Round 5	Ashford United	1	Dunston UTS	1	(aet)
Round 5	Hartley Wintney	1	Hereford	4	
Replay	Bowers & Pitsea	2	Ipswich Wanderers	1	(aet)
Replay	Dunston UTS	2	Ashford United	3	
Round 6	Hereford	3	Camberley Town	2	(aet)
Round 6	Salisbury	3	Ashford United	0	
Round 6	Morpeth Town	2	Bristol Manor Farm	0	
Round 6	Bowers & Pitsea	3	Kidlington	3	(aet)
Replay	Kidlington	0	Bowers & Pitsea	4	
Semi-finals					
1st leg	Hereford	1	Salisbury	0	
2nd leg	Salisbury	1	Hereford	2	
	Hereford won 3-1 on aggregate				
1st leg	Bowers & Pitsea	2	Morpeth Town	2	
2nd leg	Morpeth Town	2	Bowers & Pitsea	1	
	Morpeth Town won 4-3 on aggregate				
FINAL	Morpeth Town	4	Hereford	1	

National League Fixtures 2016/2017 season	Aldershot Town	Barrow	Boreham Wood	Braintree Town	Bromley	Chester	Dagenham & Redbridge	Dover Athletic	Eastleigh	Forest Green Rovers	Gateshead	Guiseley	Lincoln City	Macclesfield Town	Maidstone United	North Ferriby United	Solihull Moors	Southport	Sutton United	Torquay United	Tranmere Rovers	Woking	Wrexham	York City
Aldershot Town		11/02	03/12	29/04	25/02	10/09	21/03	17/04	22/11	04/10	24/09	29/10	04/03	19/11	09/08	27/08	08/10	07/01	18/03	08/04	03/09	26/12	13/08	28/01
Barrow	06/08		10/09	27/08	03/09	16/08	18/03	29/04	29/10	28/01	26/12	22/11	07/01	04/10	08/10	17/04	19/11	03/12	04/03	18/02	04/02	08/04	21/03	24/09
Boreham Wood	13/09	17/12		29/11	04/03	20/08	14/04	04/02	01/01	06/08	22/04	18/03	21/03	01/04	29/08	22/10	21/01	19/11	22/11	17/09	16/08	29/10	01/10	18/02
Braintree Town	20/08	22/04	04/10		22/11	07/01	26/12	08/04	09/08	24/09	10/09	14/04	28/01	13/08	25/02	11/02	29/10	18/03	03/12	29/08	19/11	21/03	04/03	08/10
Bromley	16/08	14/04	12/11	28/02		25/03	24/09	25/10	29/08	07/01	20/08	22/04	08/10	10/09	03/12	11/03	18/02	28/01	26/12	04/02	06/08	04/10	08/04	26/11
Chester	17/12	25/02	29/04	17/09	19/11		09/08	01/10	18/03	03/09	11/02	13/09	29/10	21/03	13/08	29/11	01/01	22/11	27/08	08/10	04/03	14/04	21/01	08/04
Dagenham & Red.	25/10	26/11	03/09	01/01	21/01	04/02		13/09	01/04	11/03	12/11	18/02	16/08	22/10	28/02	17/09	17/12	06/08	14/04	29/11	01/10	29/04	27/08	25/03
Dover Athletic	29/08	20/08	09/08	22/10	21/03	28/01	03/12		25/02	10/09	01/04	19/11	24/09	18/03	26/12	13/08	04/03	14/04	04/10	22/04	29/10	22/11	11/02	07/01
Eastleigh	28/02	11/03	26/12	04/02	14/04	26/11	08/10	16/08		03/12	25/03	06/08	08/04	07/01	04/10	03/09	27/08	10/09	24/09	25/10	18/02	28/01	29/04	12/11
Forest Green Rovers	29/11	01/10	11/02	21/01	17/09	14/04	29/10	17/12	13/09		13/08	22/10	19/11	04/03	22/04	01/04	21/03	29/08	09/08	01/01	22/11	25/02	18/03	20/08
Gateshead	21/01	01/01	27/08	17/12	29/04	06/08	04/03	08/10	19/11	18/02		21/03	14/04	22/11	08/04	13/09	17/09	04/02	03/09	01/10	29/11	18/03	29/10	16/08
Guiseley	11/03	28/02	26/11	03/09	27/08	03/12	13/08	25/03	11/02	08/04	25/10		26/12	24/09	07/01	25/02	29/04	08/10	28/01	12/11	14/04	10/09	09/08	04/10
Lincoln City	12/11	17/09	25/10	01/10	01/04	11/03	25/02	21/01	22/10	25/03	29/08	01/01		22/04	26/11	09/08	13/09	20/08	13/08	14/04	17/12	11/02	29/11	28/02
Macclesfield Town	25/03	29/11	08/10	18/02	17/12	25/10	08/04	26/11	17/09	12/11	28/02	21/01	27/08		11/03	01/10	14/04	16/08	29/04	06/08	01/01	03/09	13/09	04/02
Maidstone United	04/02	01/04	17/04	16/08	13/09	18/02	22/11	01/01	29/11	27/08	22/10	17/09	18/03	29/10		17/12	01/10	04/03	21/03	21/01	29/04	19/11	03/09	06/08
North Ferriby United	22/04	29/08	08/04	06/08	29/10	04/10	07/01	18/02	14/04	08/10	03/12	16/08	04/02	28/01	10/09		18/03	24/09	19/11	20/08	21/03	04/03	22/11	26/12
Solihull Moors	01/04	25/03	24/09	11/03	13/08	26/12	10/09	12/11	22/04	25/10	07/01	20/08	03/12	29/08	28/01	26/11		04/10	11/02	28/02	22/10	09/08	25/02	14/04
Southport	17/09	13/09	25/03	26/11	01/10	28/02	11/02	03/09	17/12	17/04	09/08	01/04	29/04	25/02	12/11	21/01	29/11		22/10	11/03	27/08	13/08	01/01	25/10
Sutton United	26/11	12/11	28/02	13/09	01/01	22/04	29/08	29/11	21/01	04/02	14/04	01/10	18/02	20/08	25/10	25/03	06/08	08/04		16/08	17/09	08/10	17/12	11/03
Torquay United	22/10	13/08	07/01	17/04	09/08	01/04	04/10	27/08	21/03	26/12	28/01	04/03	03/09	11/02	24/09	29/04	22/11	29/10	25/02		18/03	03/12	19/11	10/09
Tranmere Rovers	14/04	09/08	25/02	25/03	11/02	12/11	28/01	11/03	13/08	28/02	04/10	29/08	10/09	26/12	20/08	25/10	08/04	22/04	07/01	26/11		24/09	08/10	03/12
Woking	01/01	22/10	11/03	25/10	29/11	29/08	20/08	28/02	04/10	16/08	26/11	17/12	06/08	14/04	25/03	12/11	04/02	18/02	01/04	13/09	21/01		17/09	22/04
Wrexham	18/02	25/10	28/01	12/11	22/10	24/09	22/04	06/08	20/08	26/11	11/03	04/02	04/10	03/12	14/04	28/02	16/08	26/12	10/09	25/03	01/04	07/01		29/08
York City	01/10	21/01	13/08	01/04	18/03	22/10	19/11	17/09	04/03	29/04	25/02	29/11	22/11	09/08	11/02	01/01	03/09	21/03	29/10	17/12	13/09	27/08	17/04	

Please note that the above fixtures may be subject to change.

National League North Fixtures 2016/2017 season	AFC Fylde	AFC Telford United	Alfreton Town	Altrincham	Boston United	Brackley Town	Bradford Park Avenue	Chorley	Curzon Ashton	Darlington 1883	FC Halifax Town	FC United of Manchester	Gainsborough Trinity	Gloucester City	Harrogate Town	Kidderminster Harriers	Nuneaton Borough	Salford City	Stalybridge Celtic	Stockport County	Tamworth	Worcester City
AFC Fylde	■	11/02	14/01	28/01	19/11	13/08	17/04	26/12	06/09	01/04	27/08	07/01	24/09	03/09	22/10	18/03	15/10	09/08	05/11	21/03	25/02	29/04
AFC Telford United	06/08	■	26/12	04/03	05/11	15/10	18/03	24/09	14/01	19/11	03/09	04/02	07/01	21/03	29/04	06/09	17/04	29/10	16/08	27/08	18/02	01/04
Alfreton Town	20/08	04/01	■	19/11	21/03	28/01	01/04	29/10	13/08	15/04	05/11	18/03	09/08	15/10	10/09	24/09	29/04	17/12	04/03	11/02	29/08	21/01
Altrincham	16/08	22/10	22/04	■	24/09	08/04	15/10	06/09	27/08	06/08	04/02	26/12	14/01	07/01	18/02	17/04	21/03	12/11	18/03	03/09	03/12	25/02
Boston United	22/04	08/04	13/09	11/03	■	12/11	06/09	14/01	03/12	18/02	22/10	03/09	26/12	17/04	04/02	27/08	25/02	25/03	06/08	07/01	16/08	08/10
Brackley Town	18/02	25/03	16/08	05/11	01/04	■	03/09	07/01	22/10	08/10	25/02	27/08	17/04	26/12	19/11	04/02	06/09	11/03	29/04	14/01	06/08	13/09
Bradford Park Avenue	29/08	08/10	12/11	25/03	21/01	17/12	■	28/01	10/08	14/09	11/03	08/04	11/02	04/03	20/08	03/12	13/08	01/01	29/10	22/04	15/04	10/09
Chorley	01/01	11/03	25/02	21/01	20/08	10/09	16/08	■	25/03	04/02	29/04	06/08	01/04	19/11	08/10	18/02	05/11	13/09	29/08	22/10	17/12	15/04
Curzon Ashton	21/01	20/08	18/02	15/04	29/04	04/03	04/02	15/10	■	15/08	19/11	20/03	29/10	01/04	17/12	06/08	18/03	29/08	01/01	24/09	10/09	05/11
Darlington 1883	12/11	22/04	27/08	11/02	13/08	18/03	21/03	09/08	28/01	■	26/12	17/04	15/10	14/01	25/02	03/09	07/01	03/12	24/09	06/09	08/04	22/10
FC Halifax Town	15/04	17/12	08/04	09/08	04/03	29/10	24/09	03/12	22/04	01/01	■	15/10	21/03	18/03	29/08	12/11	11/02	21/01	10/09	28/01	20/08	13/08
FC Utd of Manchester	10/09	09/08	08/10	01/01	17/12	15/04	05/11	11/02	13/09	29/08	25/03	■	29/04	29/10	21/01	04/03	19/11	28/01	01/04	13/08	11/03	20/08
Gainsborough Trinity	11/03	10/09	04/02	20/08	01/01	29/08	06/08	12/11	25/02	25/03	13/09	03/12	■	18/02	16/08	22/04	22/10	15/04	21/01	08/04	08/10	17/12
Gloucester City	17/12	13/09	25/03	10/09	29/08	01/01	22/10	22/04	12/11	20/08	08/10	25/02	13/08	■	11/03	08/04	09/08	11/02	15/04	03/12	21/01	28/01
Harrogate Town	04/03	03/12	07/01	13/08	09/08	22/04	14/01	18/03	03/09	29/10	17/04	06/09	28/01	24/09	■	15/10	27/08	08/04	21/03	26/12	12/11	11/02
Kidderminster Harr.	08/10	21/01	11/03	29/08	14/04	09/08	29/04	13/08	11/02	17/12	01/04	22/10	19/11	05/11	25/03	■	28/01	10/09	20/08	25/02	13/09	01/01
Nuneaton Town	25/03	29/08	03/12	13/09	29/10	21/01	18/02	08/04	08/10	10/09	06/08	22/04	04/03	04/02	15/04	16/08	■	20/08	17/12	12/11	01/01	11/03
Salford City	04/02	25/02	03/09	01/04	15/10	24/09	26/12	21/03	17/04	29/04	06/09	16/08	27/08	06/08	05/11	07/01	14/01	■	18/02	18/03	22/10	19/11
Stalybridge Celtic	08/04	28/01	22/10	08/10	11/02	03/12	25/02	17/04	26/12	11/03	07/01	12/11	06/09	27/08	13/09	14/01	03/09	13/08	■	09/08	22/04	25/03
Stockport County	13/09	15/04	06/08	17/12	10/09	20/08	19/11	04/03	11/03	21/01	16/08	18/02	05/11	29/04	01/01	29/10	01/04	08/10	04/02	■	25/03	29/08
Tamworth	29/10	13/08	17/04	29/04	28/01	11/02	27/08	03/09	07/01	05/11	14/01	24/09	18/03	06/09	01/04	21/03	26/12	04/03	19/11	15/10	■	09/08
Worcester City	03/12	12/11	06/09	29/10	18/03	21/03	07/01	27/08	08/04	04/03	18/02	14/01	03/09	16/08	06/08	26/12	24/09	22/04	15/10	17/04	04/02	■

Please note that the above fixtures may be subject to change.

National League South Fixtures 2016/2017 season

	Bath City	Bishop's Stortford	Chelmsford City	Concord Rangers	Dartford	Eastbourne Borough	East Thurrock United	Ebbsfleet United	Gosport Borough	Hampton & Richmond Borough	Hemel Hempstead Town	Hungerford Town	Maidenhead United	Margate	Oxford City	Poole Town	St. Albans City	Truro City	Wealdstone	Welling United	Weston-super-Mare	Whitehawk
Bath City		14/01	19/11	05/11	22/10	08/10	27/08	25/02	13/09	07/01	11/03	26/12	01/04	28/01	06/09	17/04	13/08	11/02	25/03	29/04	09/08	03/09
Bishop's Stortford	20/08		01/01	21/01	19/11	25/02	11/03	13/09	15/04	06/08	17/12	16/08	25/03	10/09	01/04	18/02	22/10	29/04	29/08	04/02	05/11	08/10
Chelmsford City	22/04	26/12		25/02	13/08	11/03	12/09	05/09	25/03	12/11	22/10	03/12	14/01	08/08	27/08	08/04	11/02	28/01	08/10	17/04	03/09	07/01
Concord Rangers	08/04	06/09	29/10		11/03	11/02	26/12	09/08	22/04	03/12	25/03	08/10	27/08	04/03	14/01	12/11	28/01	13/08	13/09	03/09	07/01	17/04
Dartford	04/03	22/04	18/02	24/09		08/04	07/01	26/12	16/08	17/04	12/11	27/08	03/09	21/03	29/10	03/12	15/10	18/03	06/08	06/09	14/01	04/02
Eastbourne Borough	18/03	29/10	24/09	16/08	05/11		17/04	27/08	18/02	04/02	06/08	14/01	06/09	15/10	03/09	07/01	29/04	04/03	01/04	21/03	19/11	26/12
East Thurrock United	15/04	24/09	21/03	01/01	10/09	29/08		22/10	20/08	18/02	04/02	06/08	05/11	21/01	18/03	25/02	19/11	17/12	29/04	16/08	15/10	01/04
Ebbsfleet United	29/10	21/03	21/01	04/02	01/01	15/04	04/03		17/12	15/10	20/08	18/02	19/11	29/08	29/04	06/08	24/09	05/11	10/09	01/04	18/03	16/08
Gosport Borough	21/03	27/08	15/10	19/11	11/02	13/08	14/01	03/09		06/09	25/02	07/01	28/01	24/09	17/04	26/12	18/03	09/08	22/10	05/11	01/04	29/04
Hampton & Richmond	10/09	28/01	01/04	29/04	29/08	09/08	13/08	25/03	21/01		01/01	11/03	22/10	11/02	05/11	08/10	17/12	20/08	15/04	19/11	25/02	13/09
Hemel Hempstead Tn	24/09	03/09	04/03	15/10	01/04	28/01	09/08	14/01	29/10	26/12		17/04	11/02	18/03	13/08	27/08	21/03	19/11	05/11	07/01	29/04	06/09
Hungerford Town	01/01	11/02	29/04	18/03	15/04	20/08	28/01	13/08	10/09	24/09	29/08		25/02	17/12	08/08	22/10	01/04	21/01	19/11	15/10	20/03	05/11
Maidenhead United	12/11	15/10	20/08	15/04	17/12	21/01	08/04	22/04	06/08	04/03	16/08	29/10		03/12	21/03	04/02	10/09	29/08	01/01	18/03	24/09	18/02
Margate	06/08	07/01	04/02	22/10	13/09	25/03	06/09	17/04	11/03	16/08	08/10	03/09	29/04		19/11	14/01	05/11	01/04	18/02	26/12	27/08	25/02
Oxford City	21/01	12/11	15/04	20/08	25/02	17/12	08/10	03/12	29/08	08/04	18/02	02/04	13/09	22/04		25/03	01/01	10/09	16/08	06/08	22/10	11/03
Poole Town	29/08	13/08	05/11	01/04	29/04	10/09	29/10	28/01	01/01	18/03	15/04	04/03	09/08	20/08	15/10		21/01	21/03	17/12	24/09	11/02	19/11
St. Albans City	18/02	04/03	16/08	06/08	25/03	03/12	22/04	11/03	08/10	03/09	13/09	12/11	07/01	08/04	26/12	06/09		29/10	04/02	14/01	17/04	27/08
Truro City	16/08	03/12	06/08	18/02	08/10	22/10	03/09	08/04	04/02	14/01	22/04	06/09	17/04	12/11	07/01	13/09	25/02		11/03	27/08	26/12	25/03
Wealdstone	15/10	17/04	18/03	20/03	28/01	12/11	03/12	07/01	04/03	27/08	08/04	22/04	26/12	13/08	11/02	03/09	08/08	24/09		29/10	05/09	14/01
Welling United	03/12	09/08	29/08	17/12	21/01	13/09	11/02	12/11	08/04	22/04	10/09	25/03	08/10	01/01	28/01	11/03	20/08	15/04	25/02		13/08	22/10
Weston-super-Mare	04/02	08/04	17/12	10/09	20/08	22/04	25/03	08/10	12/11	29/10	03/12	13/09	11/03	15/04	04/03	16/08	29/08	01/01	21/01	18/02		06/08
Whitehawk	17/12	18/03	10/09	29/08	10/08	01/01	12/11	11/02	03/12	22/03	21/01	08/04	13/08	29/10	24/09	22/04	15/04	15/10	20/08	04/03	28/01	

Please note that the above fixtures may be subject to change.

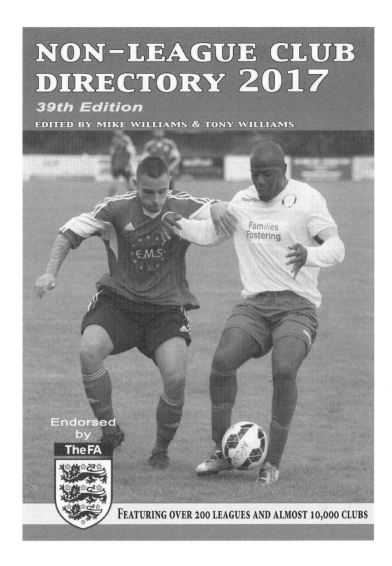

NON-LEAGUE CLUB DIRECTORY 2017

39th Edition

EDITED BY MIKE WILLIAMS & TONY WILLIAMS

Families Fostering

E.M.S

Endorsed by
The FA

FEATURING OVER 200 LEAGUES AND ALMOST 10,000 CLUBS

Now in its 39th year of publication, The Directory has developed into a comprehensive record of competitions within the non-league game and gives this level of football the publicity and prestige it deserves.

The Football Association has encouraged the development of the publication since its introduction as a small pocket book in 1978 and all their competitions such as The Cup, Trophy and Vase plus their Youth and Women's cups are featured.

Individual club pages highlight the top twelve divisions with club details, records and statistics plus senior players are featured in team photographs and within many action shots from league and cup football.

Major competitions within the nation's pyramid of domestic leagues are featured from levels 1-7 with many leagues outside of the top seven steps also featured.

Supporters' Guides and Tables books

Our Supporters' Guide series has been published since 1982 and the new 2017 editions contain the 2015/2016 Season's results and tables, Directions, Photographs, Telephone numbers, Parking information, Admission details, Disabled information and much more.

Our Football Tables books are perfect companions to the Supporters' Guides and contain historical Football League, Non-League and Scottish final tables up to the end of the 2015/2016 season.

THE SUPPORTERS' GUIDE TO PREMIER & FOOTBALL LEAGUE CLUBS 2017

This 33rd edition covers all 92 Premiership and Football League clubs. *Price £9.99*

NON-LEAGUE SUPPORTERS' GUIDE AND YEARBOOK 2017

This 25th edition covers all 68 clubs in Step 1 & Step 2 of Non-League football – the Vanarama National League, National League North and National League South. *Price £9.99*

SCOTTISH FOOTBALL SUPPORTERS' GUIDE AND YEARBOOK 2017

The 24th edition featuring all Scottish Professional Football League, Highland League and Lowland League clubs. *Price £9.99*

ENGLISH FOOTBALL LEAGUE & F.A. PREMIER LEAGUE TABLES 1888-2016

The 19th edition contains every Football League & F.A. Premier League final table plus play-off results and F.A. Cup and League Cup semi-final & final results. *Price £9.99*

NON-LEAGUE FOOTBALL TABLES 1889-2016

The 14th edition contains final league tables for the National League (formerly the Football Conference) and its 3 feeder leagues, the Northern Premier League, Southern League and Isthmian League. This edition also contains tables for the Eastern Counties League 1935-2016 and the South Midlands Spartan League 1997-2016 *Price £9.99*

SCOTTISH FOOTBALL TABLES 1890-2016

The 5th edition contains final league tables for all Scottish Professional Football League, Scottish League, Scottish Premier League, Highland League and Lowland Football League seasons. *Price £9.99*

These books are available UK & Surface post free from –

Soccer Books Limited (Dept. SBL)
72 St. Peter's Avenue
Cleethorpes, DN35 8HU
United Kingdom